Wild flowers
of
Greece

By GEORGE SFIKAS

With 135 illustrations in colour
8 coloured drawings and 8 line drawings
by the Author

ATHENS

EFSTATHIADIS GROUP S.A.
14, Valtetsiou Str.
106 80 Athens
Tel: (01) 5154650, 6450113
Fax: (01) 5154657
GREECE

ISBN 960 226 061 0

Printed and bound in Greece

INTRODUCTION

The foreign visitor roaming over Greece soon discovers its lack of extensive forests. There is, proportionately, less forest in this land of the Eastern Mediterranean than in any other European country.

This bareness of the land is not natural but the result of man's activity. Many millenia ago, nearly all of Greece was covered by immense forests, but these were gradually destroyed by fire as the inhabitants cleared the land to make it suitable for grazing and cultivation. And what man did not destroy deliberately was destroyed by fire accidentally during the hot, dry summer months. Today, apart from the steepest mountain slopes where agriculture and grazing are not possible and forests are free from depredation, a tree-covered landscape is a rare sight.

Yet as bare as the land may seem, Greece is wealthy in the diversity of its flora, possessing at least 6,000 species, not to mention still more numerous sub-species. Many genera, such as *Dianthus, Viola, Campanula, Gentaurea* and *Colchicum*, are each represented by hundreds of species.

Among European countries only Spain, with its greater land area, exceeds Greece in the diversity of its flora, while Crete alone has almost as many plant species —more than two thousand— as Great Britain, though Crete is 35 times smaller.

This wealth of flora is due to Greece's geographical position at the crossroads of three continents, to the plenitude of its islands, to the high mainland mountains which separate the country into thousands of botanically isolated valleys, large and small, and to the great differences in climate from one region to another.

Nevertheless, what makes Greece such a paradise for both botanists and amateur flower lovers alike is not the great variety of species but their rarity. Nearly a tenth of Greek flora is endemic and not to be found anywhere else in the world. Many

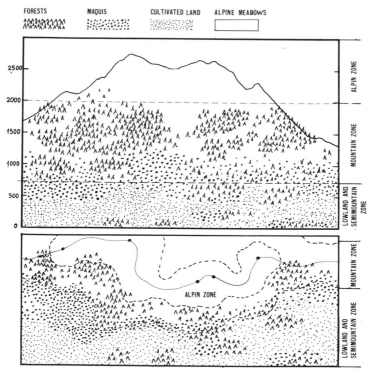

FORESTS MAQUIS CULTIVATED LAND ALPINE MEADOWS

An example of different types of vegetation in the area of a mountainous part

rare Alpine plants and numerous Asiatic species are also found here.

Except for a few hundred species of trees and tall shrubs, the flora of Greece consists of bushes, herbs and other plants, both annuals and perennials, which usually have striking flowers.

Annuals of lower altitudes germinate in late autumn, grow during the winter and flower during springtime. In the summer

6

heat they dry up and shed their seeds on the soil. On the other hand, mountain annuals appear in the spring as the snow melts away, then flower in summer and dry up at the onset of winter.

Perennials of the lowlands and hills employ a variety of devices by which they can withstand the summer drought: deep roots, bulbs, tubers, etc. Perennial alpine plants have no problem during the summer when the climate is cool and moist at high altitudes, though they do have to survive under the deep layers of snow which carpet everything for almost five months during the winter. Most of them lose those parts exposed above the surface: only the root lives on, protected under a stone or in a rock fissure. Some plants such as *Saxifraga,* are round and compact with dense stems and thorny leaves which protect the root, while others, like the *Sempervivum,* have succulent leaves, or they are covered with very dense hair.

We usually consider Greece to be a Mediterranean country with a neverending summer, and that the sea is its main characteristic. Greece, however, has high mountains some of which are over 2,000 meters where the climate is similar to that of Northern Europe.

The mountains of Greece are a continuation of the Dinaric Alps which in turn are an extension of the main Alps. The main mountain chain of Greece is the Pindos which runs from north to south, dividing the country into eastern and western parts. The Pindos chain is continued south by the Agrafa (South Pindos) range, and is then further extended by the mountains of Central Greece (Roumeli), which terminate in Attica. The mountains of the Peloponnese are also part of this same geological bow which, after rising from the sea to form the island of Kythera, sweeps eastwards to form the mountains of Crete. Indeed, with the exception of the islands of the northwestern and northeastern Aegean (which belong geologically to Asia Minor), all the islands of Greece and all the mountains of the mainland are branches or prolongations of the main Pindos chain.

The plants of Greece can be divided into five groups according

The main mountains in Greece.

to their climatic and soil preferences: a) aquatic plants, b) plants of the littoral zone, c) plants of the lowlands and semi-mountain zone, d) plants of the mountain zone, and e) plants of the alpine zone.

Aquatic plants are found where water is in abundance, as in lakes, marshes, rivers and springs. The same species are often met with near the sea and at high altitudes as well.

Plants which cannot survive far from the seashore are classed as belonging to the littoral zone, though additionally there are other species, such as *Malcolmia maritima, Mathiola sinuata, Glaucium flavum* and *Pankratium maritimum,* which prefer the littoral environment without being absolutely dependent on it.

The lowland and semi-mountain zone begins almost at sea level and rises to an altitude of 700 metres. Plains, hills and the lower mountain slopes are included in this zone. Extensive forests of pine and oak trees covered these areas in earlier times. The clearing of these areas for cultivation and grazing has changed their aspect completely. Also, the new agricultural character of the landscape favoured the rapid extension of some species as others were displaced. Genera met with in this zone are typically Mediterranean, such as *Papaver, Anemone, Chrysanthemum, Anthemis* and *Cistus*.

The mountain zone begins at an altitude of 700 metres and extends to an altitude of 2,200 metres. Virtually all of the remaining forests of Greece are found in this zone. They usually consist of various coniferous trees, pines, firs, etc., as well as beeches, oaks and other deciduous trees. Some species of small plants are given shelter in the forest shades, among them species of the genera *Lilium, Cyclamen, Primula* and *Lonicera,* all with fascinating flowers.

The alpine zone is characterised by an absolute lack of forests (Fig. 1), which is due to the severe climatic conditions. This zone theoretically starts at an altitude of 2,300-2,400 metres, but on most mountains it in fact starts much lower, sometimes as low as 2,000 metres. This extension of the alpine meadows to include normally forested areas is technical and due to the systematic burning of the highest regions by shepherds who wished to create new fields suitable for grazing their animals. Centuries of burning and grazing have prevented the regeneration of the trees to this day.

An amazing number of rare herbs or bushy plants attempt to survive in the alpine zone where everything is covered with snow from December until May. Each of them has its own way of surviving during the difficult winter period.

From the foregoing, it is clear that spring does not arrive simultaneously in every region. Shorelines which are dry during the summer become green during the winter and by February they are ornamented with spring colours. April is the month during which most wild flowers blossom, and as the days pass, spring advances towards the *maquis* (or brushwood) localities of the semi-mountain zone.

Flowering in the semi-mountain zone begins by the middle of May, but June is the best month. Early flowers of the alpine zone appear gradually through June, but July is a month of flowering fiesta as nine out of ten plants are in bloom.

August is undoubtedly the month with the fewest flowers, due to the drought and great heat in the lower regions. Even in the mountains, August is the hottest and driest month.

A short second spring begins in September. *Colchicums, Sternbergias* and *Cyclamens* blossom in the mountain zone, while many plants of the alpine zone revive and flower again. This blossoming lasts up to October when the first winter frost stops any activity in the mountains while life returns to the lowlands.

Several localities in the mountains and on the islands of Greece are paradises for botanical studies because of the rarity of the plants growing there. On the mainland these include the peaks of Olympus, Vardoussia, Chelmos, Taïyetos, Athos and many other places along the Pindos chain. The mountains of Crete, Rhodes, Samos and other islands are also worthy of renown.

But Greece has no laws protecting these places and their rare plants from despoilation. Excessive sheep-grazing in summer, the construction of roads on almost every mountain, and the sometimes indiscriminate collecting of rare plants by foreign scientists are endangering the future of the rare wild flowers of Greece.

That is why I hope readers of this book will use it as a guide to identify and admire, but not to destroy, the rare wild flowers of my country.

George Sfikas

A typical Greek landscape in the area of the ranges called Agrapha.

The map above shows the twelve regions of Greece. The abbreviations given are used systematically throughout the text.

THR. ..... THRACE
E.M. ..... E. MACEDONIA
C.M. ..... C. MACEDONIA
W.M. ..... W. MACEDONIA
EP. .... EPIRUS
THE. ..... THESSALIA

C.GR. .... CENTRAL GREECE
PEL. ..... ⌐PELOPONNESE
CY. ...... CYCLADES
CR. ...... CRETE
N.E. AE ... N.E. AEGEAN
S.E. AE ... S.E. AEGEAN

12

GLOSSARY OF TERMS

Alternate	Leaves placed singly, at different heights on a stem (1).
Annual	A plant completing its life and seeding in one year or less.
Anther	The part of the stamen containing the pollen grains (2).
Ascending	Rising upwards at an angle.
Biennial	A plant which feeds and grows in the first year, and fruits in the second year.
Bifurcate	Forked, with two equal branches (3).
Bipartite	Deeply divided into two, to below the middle (4).
Bipinnate	Twice cut; of leaves cut into distinct segments which are themselves cut into distinct segments (5).
Bulb	A swollen underground bud-like structure, remaining dormant below ground during unfavourable growth periods (6).
Calyx, Calyces	The sepals collectively; often joined together in a tube, the calyx tube (7).
Campanulate	A calyx or corolla which has the shape of a bell.
Capitulum	A head of small stalkless flowers crowded together at the end of the stem, as in Compositae (8).
Capsule	A dry fruit formed from two or more fused carpels which splits open when ripe (9).
Cordate	Heart-shaped leaf (14).
Corolla	The petals collectively; often joined together into a tube, the corolla tube (10).
Corona	Structures or appendages which stand out from the petals and together form a ring round the center of the flower (11).
Dichotomous	Divided into two equal forks, and often forked again and again (12).
Elliptic	Oval and narrowed to rounded ends in profile (13).
Entire	Leaf without teeth, lobes or indentations at its margin.

Epicalyx	A calyx-like structure outside, but close to the true calyx (15).
Evergreen	Remaining green throughout the year, particularly of leaves that persist on the stem throughout the winter or dry season.
Filament	The slender stalk of the stamen, which bears the anthers (16).
Floret	A small flower, usually one of a dense cluster, as in compositae (17).
Flower	The reproductive part of certain plants, usually comprising sepals, petals, stamens, and ovary.
Flower stalk	Slender stem bearing the flowers.
Glandular, Gland	Organs of secretion usually on the tips of hairs, hence glandular-hairs (18).
Lance-shaped, lanceolate	Shaped like a lance with the broadest part nearer the base, with an acute apex and regularly narrowed to the base (19).
Leaflet	The individual part of a compound leaf which is usually leaf-like and possesses its own stalk (20).
Linear	Long and narrow, with parallel sides (21).
Lobe	A part or segment of an organ deeply divided from the rest of the organ but not separated from it (22).
Maquis	A thicket of tall shrubs and scattered trees characteristically developed in a Mediterranean climate.
Margins	The lips, the outline border of the leaves and of the petals.
Nerve	Prominent veins in a leaf or petal (23).
Oblong	An elongated but relatively wide shape, as in a leaf with parallel sides (24).
Opposite	Of two organs; arising at the same level on opposite sides of the stem (25).
Ovary	The part of the flower containing the ovules and later the seeds, usually with one or more styles and stigmas (26).
Ovate	With an outline like that of a hen's egg, with the broadest part towards the base (27).
Palmate	Lobed or divided in a palm-like or hand-like manner (28).

14

Palmately-lobed	Lobed in a palm-like shape.
Papillate	Having small rounded or cylindrical protuberances.
Perennial	Living for more than two years and usually flowering each year.
Perfoliate	Of a leaf or bract with its base united round the stem (29).
Perianth *perianth segments*	The outer non-sexual parts of the flower, usually composed of two whorls, often with the outer sepals green, or both coloured (30). The perianth segments are the individual organs comprising the two whorls.
Petal	An individual member of the inner set of sterile organs surrounding the sexual parts of the flower, usually brightly coloured (31).
Petiol	A small and thin stem bearing the leaf.
Pinnate	The regular arrangement of leaflets in two rows on either side of the stalk of rachis (32).
Pinnatifid or pinnately lobed	A leaf with opposite pairs of deep lobes cut nearly to the midvein (33)
Ray florets	The strap-shaped florets of many members of the compositae (34).
Reinforme	Reins-shaped leaves.
Rhizome	A creeping underground stem which sends up new leaves and stems each season (36).
Scale	Any thin dry flap of tissue; usually a modified or degenerate leaf(37); also see cone.
Sepal	One of the outer set of perianth segments, usually green and protecting in bud, less commonly coloured and petal-like (38).
Sessile	Leaf or flower not borne on a stalk.
Solitary	Flower borne at the end of the stem or at its axils.
Spathe	A large bract enclosing a flower head; it is sometimes conspicuous and coloured, or papery (39)
Spathulate	Spoon or paddle-shaped; broadest towards the apex and narrowed to the base (40).

Spike	A slender elongated cluster of more or less stalkless flowers, the youngest flowers at the apex, the oldest at the base (41).
Spur	A hollow, more or less cylindrical projection from a petal or sepal; it usually contains nectar (42).
Stamen	One of the male reproductive organs of the flower, which bears the pollen (2 and 16).
Sticky or limy	The segment of the plant which sticks when touched.
Stigma	The part of the female organ which receives the male pollen (43).
Stipule, Stipulate	A scale-like or leaf like appendage at the base of the leaf-stalk; usually paired (44).
Style	A more or less elongated projection of the ovary which bears the stigma (45).
Sword shaped	Elongated, narrow and acute sword-like leaf (46).
Three-lobed	Leaf or sepal divided in three lobes (47).
Throat	The opening or orifice of a tubular of funnel-shaped corolla, or calyx (48).
Tooth	Tooth shape usually formed at the margin of petals or leaves (49).
Toothed	With small triangular or rounded projections on a margin or rib (49).
Tube	The fused part of the calyx or corolla (50).
Tuber	A swollen part of a stem or root, formed annually and usually underground (51).
Two-lipped	A tube corolla forming two lobes at its orifice, upper and lower.
Umbel	A cluster of flowers whose spreading stalks arise from the apex of the stem, resembling the spokes of an umbrella (52).
Whorl	More than two organs of the same kind arising from the same level; thus whorled (53).

16

1

1. CYTINUS RUBER *Fourr. Komarov*
Family: Rafflesiaceae (Cytinaceae)
Modern Greek Name: Lykos tou Ladanou

The genus *Cytinus* includes parasites living on roots of other plants. The species illustrated, one of two which are native to Greece, is widespread in brushwood localities of low altitude. It is a parasite on the roots of the pink or purple flowered Cistus. Its fleshy stems have a reddish hue and grow up to 12 cm. high. The red or deep purple leaves are reduced to scales. The flowers grow 5-10 together at the end of the stems. Lower flowers are female, upper flowers are male. The perianth is tubular or campanulate with four lobes of a yellowish white or pink white colour. Flowers May-June. Common almost everywhere in Greece.

2. MINUARTIA STELLATA *Mair.* SUBSP. STELLATA
Family: Caryophyllaceae

The genus *Minuartia* includes small perennial or annual plants with linear or lance-shaped opposite leaves and always white flowers with

2.

5 sepals and 5 petals. The short stems are so dense that the whole of the plant looks like a green swelling. The lance-shaped to triangular leaves are stiff and sharply pointed. The flowers are solitary or grow in couples at the end of slender stalks. Flowers July-August. EP. THE.-C.GR.- PEL.

3. SAPONARIA OFFICINALIS *L.*
Family: Caryophyllaceae
Modern Greek Names: Sapounohorto, Tsoueni

The genus *Saponaria* includes annual or perennial species producing opposite leaves and flowers on dichotomous stems. The calyx is tubular and 5-toothed at the opening. Five petals usually entire, with scales on the inner surface. The species illustrated is a perennial with creeping rhizome and many branches erect, stout, simple, 30-60 cm. high. Leaves rather big, opposite, lanceolate-ovate with acute tips and 3 to 5 parallel veins. Flowers in pale pink or white are large and grow on short stalks in lax terminal clusters. The plant grows in the mountain and semi-mountain zones. It is also cultivated. Well known since

3

4

ancient times due to its pharmaceutical properties this plant was used as a purgative, an appetizer and against rheumatism. Flowers June-September. Widely distributed almost everywhere in Greece.

4. SAPONARIA HAUSSKNECHTII *Simmler*
Family: Caryophyllaceae

Rare plant found in the mountain zone of Albania and northwestern Greece. Stems grow up to 50 cm. in height. Leaves opposite, the upper ones borne on a short stalk are lanceolate while the lower ones borne on a longer stalk are lanceolate to oblong. The relatively big flowers are borne on loose dichotomous stalks on the end of the branches. Flowers June-September. EP. W.M.

5. CERASTIUM CANDIDISSIMUM *Correns.*
Family: Caryophyllaceae

Annual or perennial bushy plants are included in the genus *Cerastium*. They have small leaves, usually opposite, entire and elongated, with white flowers at the tips of dichotomous branches. The species illus-

5

trated is a perennial endemic to Greece. It grows on rocks in the alpine zone. A dense down covers the plant and gives it a greyish-green colour. Its more or less erect stems form a big bouquet. Lower leaves are oblong-spathulate in contrast to the upper ones which are linear-lanceolate. The flowers are big with bipartite petals twice as long as the sepals. It flowers May-July. EP.- THE.- C.GR.- PEL.

6. DIANTHUS BIFLORUS *S & S*
Family: Caryophyllaceae
Modern Greek Name: Agriogarifalo

The genus *Dianthus* is richly represented in Greek flora by more than 60 species. The name Dianthus (meaning "flower of Zeus") was given to these flowers because they were dedicated to the supreme god of the Olympian pantheon. Different species display a variation of red, pink or white flowers. Petals five, usually toothed. Calyx tubular, five-toothed, its base closely encircled by the scales of the epicalyx. The shape, the size and the number of these scales help to identify

6

7

each species. *Dianthus biflorus* is one of the most attractive species of the genus. Relatively big flowers, almost 2cm., are borne, usually in couples, on the tip of the stems 40cm high. Petals of a red hue on the upper surface are yellowish beneath. Leaves narrow, linear, 5-15cm. across, 1-3mm. wide. The plant grows on waste land of mountaine zone. Flowers June-August. EP.- THE.- C.GR.- PEL.

7. **DIANTHUS CARTHUSIANORUM** *L.*
Family: Caryophyllaceae

Perennial species encountered towards the northern boundaries of the country but only rarely. Branches numerous, almost 60 cm. high, and leaves narrow-linear. Flowers are clustered in dense heads on the end of the stems. It grows in mountain woods. Flowers June-September C.M.- W.M.- EP.

8. **DRYPIS SPINOSA** *L.* SUBSP. **SPINOSA**
Family: Caryophyllaceae

The species illustrated along with two subspecies is the sole representative of the genus. It is a small thorny bush forming tiny hummocks

among the rocks and pebbles of the alpine zone. Leaves opposite, stiff and thorny. White or pale pink flowers with bipartite petals are borne in terminal inflorescences. Flowers July-August. W.M.- EP.- THE.- C.GR.- PEL.

9. PAEONIA CLUSII *F.C. Stearn* S.SP. RHODIA (W.T. Stearn) Tzan.
Family: Paeoniaceae

Paeonias as well as liliums are undoubtedly the most captivating wild flowers of the Greek mountains. Many species and subspecies of the genus are represented in Greek flora but their scientific identification has not yet been completed. *Paeonia rhodia,* endemic to the island of Rhodes, grows in profusion on Mount Prophet Elias. Its large, sparkling white flowers 8-9cm. in diameter are scented like cinnamon. Leaves are cut in many elongated segments. Flowers March-April. S.E.AE. (RHODES).

10. ANEMONE BLANDA *Schott & Kotschy*
Family: Ranunculaceae Modern Greek Name: Anemona tou Vounou

Small plants with palmately lobed or deeply dissected leaves are inc-

10   11

luded in the genus *Anemone*. The tuberous rhizome gives rise to long
petiols bearing the leaves. Flowers usually solitary on an unbranched
long stem. A whorl of 3 leaves is always placed some way below the
flower. Characteristic feature of the blooms is the complete absence
of petals. On the contrary the sepals of the flower are big and brightly
coloured. The Flowers of the species illustrated show every colour
variation from deep purple to pink and white. Numerous sepals 10-18,
make it reminiscent of a blue daisy. Basal leaves palmately lobed in
segments further deeply cut thrice into toothed lobes, are similar to
stem leaves. Plant widespread in the woods of the mountain zone.
Flowers March-June THR.- E.M. C.M.- W.M.- EP.- THE.- C.GR.-
PEL.- CR.- CY.

11. ANEMONE PAVONINA *Lam*. VAR. PURPUREO-VIOLACEA *Boiss*.

Family: Ranunculaceae
Modern Greek Names: Anemona, Agrolales

Species producing large beautiful flowers 4-5cm. in diameter. Sepals

12

7-9. Stem leaves are sessile, entire lance-shaped sometimes slightly trilobate at the tips. Basal leaves are toothed three-lobated. Species met with growing on wasteland and in brushwood localities of low altitude. It displays great variety of form. One of the numerous varieties is the one illustrated producing purple-mauve flowers. Flowers early in the spring from February-April. Widespread throughout Greece.

12. RANUNCULUS BREVIFOLIUS *Ten*. SUBSP. PINDICUS *(Hausskn). E. Mayer*
Family: Ranunculaceae

The genus *Ranunculus* is extensively represented in Greece. It includes almost 60 species, some of which are found growing in meadows and others in still or slow flowing waters. Flowers usually yellow or white and occasionally reddish. Petals 5 or more, sepals 3 to 5, small. The species illustrated is found growing in the alpine zone among stones and pebbles. Leaves 3-5 lobed usually positioned near

the base of the stem. Yellow flowers, solitary, at the end of the stems. Flowers May-July. W.M. -EP. -THE. -C.GR. -PEL.

13. RANUNCULUS ASIATICUS *L.*
Family: Ranunculaceae
Modern Greek Name: Neragoula

The most captivating species of the genus found in Greece. Big flowers displaying a colour range from white to bright red are borne 1 to 4 together on each stem. Leaves palmately dissected in numerous fine lobes further cut into smaller segments. It is found growing in brushwood and on fields of the lowland or of the semi-mountain zone. Flowers March-May. PEL. (KYTHIRA) - CR. - S.E. AE. This sometimes found growing elsewhere as well.

14. AQUILEGIA OTHONIS *Orph.*
Family: Ranunculaceae

Species included in the genus *Aquilegia* are perennials having numer-

14

15

ous erect stems and abundant large flowers with 5 petals and 5 coloured sepals with long backward-projecting spurs. Leaves long-
stalked, each leaflet further cut into many segments forming a fan.
The species illustrated is one of the most beautiful and rarest in
Greece. It is met with only on the mountains of the Peloponnese and
occasionally in the mountains of Central Greece. It is also found in
southern Italy. The most distinctive feature of the plant are the hook-
like curved spurs and the colour of the flowers: generally bluish with
lighter petals. Flowers June-July. C.GR.- PEL.

15. AQUILEGIA AMALIAE *Heldr*.
Family: Ranunculaceae

Species similar to the preceding one, the difference lying in the more
elaborately dissected leaves, the almost straight spurs and the colour
of the sepals which display a range from pale pink to bluish-mauve in
contrast to the almost white petals. Rare species encountered on the
wooded heights of Mount Olympus and a few other mountains nearby.
Flowers May-July. C.M.- W.M.- THE.

26

16

16. PAPAVER RHOEAS *L.*
Family: Papaveraceae
Modern Greek Name: Paparouna

Ephemeral blossoms with 4 big petals and 2 sepals shedding as soon as they are open are the characteristic features of the genus *Papaver*. The illustrated species is undoubtedly the most beautiful of the 11 of which the genus is composed. It is an annual plant with bipinnate leaves borne on pubescent stems 20-60cm. high. Petals of brilliant scarlet have a black spot at their base. It is found growing amidst brushwood and in fields of low altitude or of the mountain zone. Flowers April-June. Occurs throughout Greece.

17. AUBRIETIA DELTOIDEA *D.C.*
Family: Cruciferae

Aubrietias are perennial pubescent or hairy plants. Flowers with 4 sepals and 4 petals usually mauve or more seldom almost white. The species illustrated produces numerous dense branches on the tips of

which are borne the flower clusters. Leaves covered with down of a greyishgreen colour have the shape of the Greek letter Delta, hence the name Deltoidea. It establishes itself in rock fissures of the mountain and alpine zones. Flowers April-June. C.M.- W.M.- EP.- THE.- C.GR.- PEL.- CR.- N.E.AE.- S.E.AE.

18. SAXIFRAGA SCARDICA *Criseb.*

Family: Saxifragaceae

Annual or perennial plants with rather small flowers of varying colour. Petals 5, sepals 5. More than 20 species of the genus are met with in Greece. One of the most beautiful is the species illustrated. Its exceedingly dense branches form a compact rosette. Leaves small, reduced to scales, stiff, sharp-pointed and very dense. Flowers borne in terminal clusters on the tip of the stems growing to 10cm. Petals white or pinkish 2 to 4 times as long as the sepals. It establishes itself in rock

fissures of the mountain and alpine zones. Flowers June-August.
C.M.- W.M.- EP.- THE.- C.GR.- PEL.

19. SAXIFRAGA SIBTHORPII *Boiss*.
Family: Saxifragaceae

Perennial species with succulent leaves dissected into 5 to 7 lobes.
Stems tender up to 15cm. high, prostrate or ascending. Flowers in
profusion, small in a golden-yellow colour. It establishes itself in rock
fissures in damp and cool localities. Flowers June-August. C.GR.-
PEL.

20. PARNASSIA PALUSTRIS *L*.
Family: Saxifragaceae

The sole representative of this genus bearing the name of Mt. Parnas-
sus growing in this country. It has a perennial rhizome, leaves ovate to
cordate, long stalked, rising straight from the base. The stem grows

20   21

10-30cm. high and bears a single sessile leaf. Flowers white, solitary, big with 5 petals. It grows in the mountain and alpine zones, thriving on sunny, very damp wasteland. Flowers July to September. THR.- E.M.- C.M.- W.M.- EP.- C.GR. PEL.

21. PRUNUS PROSTRATA *Lebill*
Family: Rosaceae

The genus *Prunus* includes common shrubs and trees. The illustrated species grows to a tiny curved shrub up to 2m high. Leaves small up to 2.5 cm. long. Its fruit is reminiscent of a small cherry but is not edible. It grows in the mountain and alpine zones. Flowers April-June. E.M. C.M. -W.M. -EP. -C. GR. PEL. CR. It can also be found elsewhere in Greece.

22. ROSA GLUTINOSA *S. & S.*
Family: Rosaceae

The genus *Rosa* is richly represented in Greek flora by many species

22

23

and subspecies. They usually grow high to shrub proportions, are more or less thorny, with pinnate leaves of 5-7 leaflets. Petals pure white, pink or reddish. The species illustrated grows as a small dense shrub. It produces stout thorns which are slightly curved or small and straight. Leaves of 5 to 7 glandular leaflets. Fruit ovate covered with glandular hairs. Flowers April-June. It is found on rocky fallow lands and forests of the mountain zone. E.M.-C.M.-W.M.-EP.-THE.-C.GR.-PEL.-CR.

23. ROSA ARVENSIS *Hudson*
Family: Rosaceae

Shrub with clambering slender stems and compound leaves. Leaflets 5-7 have down on the under surface. Flowers white, solitary, borne on glandular stalks. Fruit small, ovate, of reddish colour. It occurs in mountain woods. Flowers June-July. Beautiful hybrids of this species have been produced from its cross with *Rosa gallica and Rosa chinensis.* THR.-E.M.-C.M.-W.M.-EP.THE.C.GR.-PEL.

24

24. TRIFOLIUM UNIFLORUM *L.*
Family: Leguminosae

Over 60 recognised species of the genus *Trifolium* are found in Greece. Leaves trifoliate with entire or slightly notched leaflets and 2 stipules at their base. Flowers butterfly-shaped like most *Leguminosae* species. Petals 5, the uppermost of which, called "petassos," is much bigger than the remaining four. The species illustrated is a perennial which creeps along the ground. Its flowers are borne solitary on short stalks rising straight from the base. It is found in mountain meadows. Flowers June-July. C.GR.-PEL.-CY-CR.

25. TRIFOLIUM PURPUREUM *Loisel.*
Family: Leguminosae

Annual species with erect, stiff, hairy stems. Leaves of narrow acute-pointed leaflets. Flowers of pinkish colour are borne in oblong or conical clusters at the end of the stems. They open upwards from below. It frequents sunny meadows and pasture land of the mountain

25

26

zone. Flowers May-July. THR. - E.M. - C.M. - W.M. - EP. - THE. -
C.GR. - PEL.

26. SPARTIUM JUNCEUM *L.*

Family: Leguminosae
Modern Greek Name: Sparto

This perennial shrub growing up to 3m. high is the sole representative
of its genus. Leaves small, entire, oblong, usually absent make their
appearance occasionally when spring is exceedingly wet. They are
borne on branches slender, stiff, sharply pointed, green, produced in
abundance. Bright yellow, butterfly-shaped flowers slightly scented,
2.5 cm. across, forming a spike at the end of the stems. It occurs in
brushwood localities of the mountain and semi-mountain zones.
Flowers from May-July. Ubiquitous.

27. LINUM LEUCANTHUM *Boiss. & Sprun.*

Family: Linaceae

Approximately 30 species of the genus *Linum* flourish in Greece.

33

27

They are perennial or annual plants with alternate entire leaves and flowers in white, pinkish, yellow or bluish shades. Sepals 5, petals 5. The species illustrated is an endemic perennial producing numerous dense short stems and pure, white or pinkish-white flowers borne in clusters of 1-7 blooms borne at the end of the stems. Petals 2-2.5cm. length. It occurs on stony ground in the mountain and semi-mountain zones. Flowers April-May. THE. (SPORHADES). C.GR.- PEL.

28. LINUM ELEGANS *Sprun.*
Family: Linaceae

A perennial species with its unbranched stems 12cm. high forming a basal rosette. Flowers in terminal clusters of from 2 to 7 blooms or most rarely, 1 bloom. Petals **15-20mm.** Occurs in the alpine zone. Flowers June-July. THR. -E.M.-C.M.-W.M.-EP.-THE.-C.GR.-PEL.

29. DAPHNE OLEOIDES *Schreber*
Family: Thymelaeaceae
Modern Greek Names: Hamolia, Lykonoura

Perennial plants characteristic of scrubby vegetation are included in

34

28
29

30

the genus *Daphne*. Leaves alternate, entire. Flowers borne in dense, terminal, sometimes one-sided clusters, are long-tubed with four spreading, petal-like lobes. The species illustrated is *Daphne oleoides* bearing with its ripe, fleshy, red fruit. The flowers of this species frequenting rocky places of the alpine zone are of a white colour. Flourishes June-July. E.M.-C.M.-W.M.-EP.-THE.-C.GR.-PEL.-CR.

30. VIOLA DELPHINANTHA *Boiss*.

Family: Violaceae

Annual, biennial or perennial herbs are included in the genus *Viola*. Petals 5.2 petals being erect, 2 lateral, directed downwards, and a basal one forming an occasionally small or big spur directed backwards. Leaves with stipules. The species illustrated is a rare perennial of the alpine zone. It grows 10 cm. high, and its woody root gives rise to numerous slender stems. Leaves tiny, linear-lanceolate. Splendid flowers with very big spur in pinkish or violet hues. It is found on a few Greek mountains. Abroad it has been reported only at one place in Bulgaria. Flowers June-July. E.M.-C.M.-THE.-PEL.

31. VIOLA MAGELLENSIS *Porta & Rigo*
Family: Violaceae

Rare species of the alpine zone, it is endemic to the mountains of Greece, Albania and Italy. It is a tiny perennial with stems creeping over the stony ground. Flowers big, in pink or violet hues. Leaves ovate or oblong, entire, 0.5-1.5cm. **length,** the length of the petiol being included. Stipules have the same shape as the leaves and are of almost equal size. Spur rather big up to 10mm long. Flowers July-August. W.M.-EP.

32. VIOLA TRICOLOR *L.* SUBSP. **SUBALPINA** *Gaudin*
Family: Violaceae

The *Viola tricolor* is a very variable species of the alpine zone displaying 5 subspecies. The one illustrated grows up to 30 cm. high and produces erect or ascending branches, bearing elongated toothed leaves. Stipules repeatedly dissected. Flowers usually yellow or more seldom with the two erect petals in a light violet hue. Flowers June-August. C.M.-W.M.-EP.THE.-C.GR.-PEL.

33

VIOLA RIVINIANA *Reichenb.*
Family: Violaceae

The leaves of this plant, rather big, cordate, long-stalked, form a basal rosette. Stipules lanceolate, with fine spreading teeth. Flowers 1 to 4, 2.5cm. across with bluish-violet petals and pinkish or off white spur. They are borne on lateral-leaved branches and arise solitary, one from each axil. The leaves of the branches are similar to the basal ones. It grows in stony localities of woods in the mountain zone. Flowers April-May. THR.-E.M.-C.M.-W.M.-THE.-C.GR.-PEL.

34. VIOLA POETICA *Boiss. & Spruner*
Family: Violaceae

A little perennial with many short tender stems. Leaves oblong-ovate, long-stalked. Flowers borne 1-4 on each stem are of a bluish or bluish-violet hue, 1.5cm. wide. It is endemic to the mountains of Central Greece, establishing itself in rock fissures of the alpine zone. Flowers June-August. C. GR.

38

35. CISTUS INCANUS *L.* S. SP. **CRETICUS**
Family: Cistaceae
Modern Greek Name: Ladania

Little perennial shrubs are included in the genus *Cistus*. They have leaves opposite, ovate or lanceolate and flowers large with five petals in white, pink or rosy-purple colours. Sepals 3 to 5, stamens numerous. The *Cistus incanus* is a small hairy perennial shrub growing up to 1m. high. The flowers of a dark pink or rosy-purple colour are borne 1-3 together at the end of the branches. They are 4-5cm. wide. Sepals 5, acute. It is a variable species frequenting the clearings of brushwood localities in the lower mountain and the lowland zones. Flowers April-June. Ubiquitous in Greece.

36. EPILOBIUM ANGUSTIFOLIUM *L.*
Family: Onagraceae

More than ten species of the genus *Epilobium* are represented in Greek flora. They usually have a perennial rhizome and leaves elongated, entire or toothed. Calyx tubular, terminating in four lobes. Petals four, arising at the end of the calyx, in a pink or violet colour.

38

The species illustrated is one of the loveliest representatives of the genus. It is an erect unbranched perennial 1-2m. high. Leaves alternate, lanceolate, entire. Flowers large, rosy-purple, borne in long terminal spikes. It occurs in mountain forests, in ravines, on the banks of mountain rivers and in any damp place generally. Flowers June-September. THR. - E.M. - C.M. - W.M. - EP. THE. - C.GR.

37. ORLAYA GRANDIFLORA *(L.) Hoffm.*
Family: Umbelliferae

The inflorescences of this genus are composed of numerous small flowers arranged in an umbel. This is the characteristic feature of the family *Umbelliferae.* Each umbel is compound of 2-8 groups of flowers borne on separate branches and forming a secondary umbel. The umbels of the species illustrated are composed of 5-8 groups of flowers. The outermost flowers of each group are 7-8 times as big as the remaining. Leaves long-stalked, thrice pinnate, with linear-lanceolate segments. It inhabits sunny localities of the mountain and semi-mountain zones. Flowers June-July. THR.-E.M.-C.M.-W.M. -EP.-THE.-C.GR.-PEL.-CR.

41

39

38. ARBUTUS UNEDO *L*.
Family: Ericaceae   Modern Greek Name: Koumaria

The genus *Arbutus* includes perennial shrubs. The illustrated species, well known on account of its edible fruit the "Koumara," is one of the two representatives of the genus growing in Greece. Leaves lanceolate, usually notched, 5-8cm. long. Flowers small of a globular shape with 5 toothed margin in cream or rosy colour arise in drooping terminal clusters. Ripe fruit are of an orange-red colour 2cm. across. Flowers September-November. Ubiquitous in Greece.

39. CYCLAMEN GRAECUM *Link*
Family: Primulaceae   Modern Greek Names: Cyclamino, Cyclamia

Six species of *Cyclamen* are met with in Greece, some of them flourishing in autumn and others during spring. Long stalked leaves arise from a more or less large corm found at the root of the plant, and form a basal rosette. The same corm gives rise to long tender stems bearing solitary pending flowers with upwards-directed petals. The species illustrated is endemic to the Eastern Mediterranean region

42

40

41

and inhabits stony places of the mountain zone as well as lowland heaths. It produces a large, almost globular, corm at its root and cordate leaves of a reddish hue beneath and dark green richly marbled with silvery grey on the upper surface. Flowers September-November. C.M. - THE. - C.GR. - PEL. CR. - CY. N.E.AE. - S.E.AE. - EP.

40. CYCLAMEN PERSICUM *Mill.*

Family: Primulaceae

It is a spring flowering plant encountered in Asia Minor and in Greece. Its leaves are almost similar to the preceding one, their difference lying in the greenish colour of the under-surface of the latter. The flowers display a range of colour from deep purple to pure white. It is the ancestor of the cultivated cyclamens. Inhabits brushwood localities and pine-forested areas of low altitude. Flowers March-May. C.M. - N.E.AE. - S.E.AE. It can occur in other regions as well.

41. PRIMULA VERIS *L.*

Family: Primulaceae   Modern Greek Names: Dacraki, Panaghitsa

Perennial herbs with big elongated leaves arising in a basal rosette are

included in the genus *Primula*. The flowers are borne solitary or in clusters on leafless branches. Calyx tubular, corolla tubular as well, terminating in 5 spreading lobes bipartite or bilobed. The species illustrated is very variable. The bright yellow flowers are borne in clusters at the end of the same stem. It occurs in mountain forests. Flowers April-May. THR. E.M. -C.M.-W.M.-EP.-THE.-C.GR. -PEL.

42. STYRAX OFFICINALIS *L*.

Family: Styraceae
Modern Greek Names: Stouraki, Agriocidonia

This species is the sole representative of its genus met with in Europe. It is a shrub growing sometimes to tree-proportion: up to 7m. high. Leaves alternate, ovate, entire, are of a greyish-green colour on the upper surface and glaucus-green and hairy beneath. Corolla white, campanulate with a very short tube terminating in 5-7 lenceolate lobes. Flowers borne 3 to 6 together on the tips of the branches. It is a very ornamental species cultivated on account of its beautiful abundant flowers. It occurs in damp places such as stream and river banks or

woods of the semi-mountain zone. Flowers from April till May almost everywhere in Greece.

43. LIGUSTRUM VULGARE *L.*

Family: Oleaceae
Modern Greek Names: Agriomyrtia, Myrtolia

This deciduous shrub, sometimes growing to a small tree's proportions up to a height of 5m is the sole representative of the genus *Ligustrum* in Greek flora. Leaves opposite, lanceolate-elongated, falling late in the middle of the winter. Flowers in dense terminal clusters of tiny blooms with tubular corolla terminating in 4 spreading lobes. This species is met with in the mountain zone or in brushwood localities of low altitude wherever it can enjoy the company of other trees and shrubs. Flowers May-July almost everywhere in Greece.

44. GENTIANA VERNA *L.* SUBSP. PONTICA *(Soltok.) Huyek*

Family: Gentianaceae

The genus *Gentiana* is represented by 7 species in the flora of Greece. They are usually perennial plants producing opposite leaves and beau-

45

tiful flowers in a range of violet or bluish and more seldom yellow or purple colour. The species illustrated is a dwarf plant with its lower leaves forming a basal rosette. Branches 15cm. high, bear a few leaf couples. Flowers 2-3cm. across with tubular, five-toothed calyx. Corolla tubular with 5 spreading lobes in bluish colour. The subspecies *Pontica* differs from the others on account of its calyx being of an almost purple colour. It frequents the meadows of the alpine zone. Flowers May-August. THR. -E.M.-C.M.-W.M.-EP.-THE. C.GR.

45. VINCA MAJOR *L.*

Family: Apocynaceae
Modern Greek Name: Agriolitsa

Three species of the genus *Vinca* grow in Greece. All of them have blue or violet-blue flowers with calyx divided into 5 narrow lobes and corolla with a long tube terminating in 5 blunt spreading lobes. The species illustrated has very long stems trailing over the ground, and leaves ovate 2-4 cm length. Flowers from March to June almost everywhere in Greece.

46. CONVOLVULUS ALTHAEOIDES *L.*

Family: Convolvulaceae
Modern Greek Name: Agrio Periplocadi

The species of this genus are annual or perennial plants with long
stems creeping over the ground. Flowers beautiful, funnel shaped
opening when in sunlight. The species illustrated is a perennial with
exceedingly long hairy stems. Lower leaves cordate, blunt-toothed.
Upper leaves petiolate, palmately lobed. Flowers 3-4cm. across with
corolla darker pink in throat. It grows in low-altitude places and especially on wasteland by the sea. Flowers April-August. Everywhere in
Greece except W.M.

47. CALYSTEGIA SILVATICA *(Kit.) Griseb.*

Family: Convolvulaceae
Modern Greek Names: Periplokadi, Pericocladi

Plant similar to *Convolvulus* with large flowers up to 7cm wide and
large leaves cordate — arrow-shaped borne on a long petiol. It grows

47

48

in the forested areas of the mountain zone. Flowers May-August.
THR. - E.M. - C.M. - W.M. - EP. - THE. - C.GR. - PEL. - CR.

48. IPOMOEA STOLONIFERA *(Cyr.) J.F. Gmelin*
Family: Convolvulaceae
Modern Greek Name: Kampanakia

Perennial plant similar to the two preceding ones, with white flowers
up to 6cm. across and flowering stems rather fleshy, short. Leaves
ovate, elongated with margin usually bilobed at its end. It produces
very long sprouts bearing petiolate, palmate leaves. It is a cosmopoli-
tan maritime species widely distributed up to the littoral of South
America. It grows on sandy sea shores. Flowers September-October.
PEL. (KYTHIRA) CR. - S.E.AE. (RHODOS).

49. MACROTOMIA DENSIFLORA *(Ledeb.) Macbride,*
Family: Boraginaceae

This species is the sole representative of the Asiatic genus *Mac-*

rotomia found in Europe. It grows only on Mount Helmos of the northern Peloponnese and in a Turkish region. It is a hairy perennial with basal leaves narrow, elongated and acute-pointed, forming a grass tappet among the pebbles of the ground. Branches growing up to 25cm. high bear leaves erect smaller than the basal ones. Flowers yellow, large up to 2.5cm. wide. Corolla with a long, slender tube and five wide spreading lobes. Calyx hairy with five lobes delicately dissected up to their base. The flowers are borne in capitulum inflorescences up to 10cm. in diameter. It grows in the alpine zone and flowers in June. It is in danger of extinction. PEL. (HELMOS).

50. ALKANNA GRAECA *Boiss. & Spruner* SUBSP. GRAECA
Family: Boraginaceae

Almost 10 species of the genus *Alkanna* are included in Greek flora. They are annual or perennial plants with numerous hairy branches. Flowers in bluish, purple, or yellow shades with calyx divided into 5 sepals and corolla tubular, funnel-shaped, 5 lobed. The species illustrated is a perennial plant, 20-50cm. high with abundant lanceolate,

51

narrow leaves. Flowers borne in terminal spikes. It grows in the mountain and alpine zones. Flowers June-August. EP.-THE.-C.GR.-PEL.

51. **SOLENANTHUS STAMINEUS** *Desf.*
Family: Boraǧinaceae

A rare Asiatic species. Mount Helmos is the sole place in Europe where this plant is found growing. Perennial plant with erect branches 20-60cm. high. Basal leaves up to 30cm. across, lanceolate, narrow to their base forming a petiol. Stem leaves lanceolate, sessile, much smaller than the basal. Flowers tiny, reddish, funnel-shaped with stamens projecting out of the corolla. They are borne in terminal clusters. It grows in the mountain and alpine zones. Flowers from April-June. PEL. (HELMOS).

52. **ONOSMA** *S.S.*
Family: Boraginaceae

Approximately 15 species of the genus *Onosma* flourish in Greece. They are annual or perennial plants covered with stiff bristles. Leaves

53

54

linear, lanceolate. Flowers in yellow, white or reddish colour with tubular corolla and calyx with 5 linear lobes. The *Onosma erecta* is a perennial plant with numerous branches 10-25cm. high and yellow flowers. It is one of the many plants endemic to Greece. It frequents rocky localities of the mountain zone. Flowers May-July.

53. ONOSMA FRUTESCENS *Lam*.
Family: Boraginaceae
Modern Greek Name: Xylothroumbos

Xanthos
Apr/99

A perennial species with numerous reddish branches 20-50cm. high. Flowers yellow with reddish margin. It grows in brushwood localities of the semi-mountain zone. Flowers April-May. C.GR.-CY.-CR.-N.E.AE.-S.E.AE.

54. ONOSMA LEPTANTHA *Heldr*.
Family: Boraginaceae

A rare perennial species with numerous rather short unbranched stems and linear leaves. Corolla slender, a little longer than the calyx in

ΟΙΝΝΟΝ

a dull yellow colour. It is endemic to the mountain and alpine zones of Mount Taïyetos. Flowers June-July. PEL.

55. SALVIA GLUTINOSA *L.*
Family: Labiatae

Almost 25 species of the genus *Salvia* are found growing in Greece. They are annual or perennial strongly-smelling plants. Leaves opposite. Flowers displaying a great variety of colour. Calyx campanulate or funnel-shaped and corolla tubular with two-lipped margin. The upper lip is curved and the lower three-lobed. The species illustrated is a sticky perennial with stems 0.40-1m. high and leaves ovate arrow-shaped with heart-shaped base. The flowers are large of yellowish colour and they are borne in whorls composed of 2-6 blooms each at the upper part of the stems. It grows in shady places of the forested mountain zone. Flowers June-September. THR.- E.M.- C.M.- W.M.- EP.- THE.- C.GR.

56　　　　　　　　　　　　　　　　　　　　　57

56. CALAMINTHA GRANDIFLORA *(L.) Moench*
Family: Labiatae

The genus *Calamintha* includes biennial .or perennial plants with leaves opposite, smooth, usually toothed. Flowers large of various colours with calyx tubular, two-lipped. Corolla with long tube two-lipped. The upper lip is erect bipinnate and the lower lip is three-lobed. The illustrated species is the loveliest representative of its genus. It produces large flowers over 2.5cm. across and leaves large, ovate, nicely scented. It grows in mountain forests. Flowers June-September. THR.-E.M.-C.M.-W.M.-EP.-THE.-C.GR.-PEL.

57. MELITTIS MELISSOPHYLLUM *L*. SUBSP. ALBIDA *(Guss.)* *P.W. Ball*
Family: Labiatae

This plant is the sole representative of the genus *Melittis*. It produces a hairy stem 20-60cm. high and large leaves ovate with heart-shaped base. Flowers up to 4cm. across with campanulate calyx and two-

58

lipped corolla. The upper lip is entire in contrast to the 3-lobed lower one. There are 3 subspecies of this plant. Only the one illustrated occurs in Greece. It flourishes in mountain woods. Flowers May-July. E.M.-C.M.-EP.-THE.-C.GR.-PEL.-CR.

58. HYOSCYAMUS AUREUS *L*.
Family: Solanaceae

The species included in the genus *Hyoscyamus* are heavy smelling annual or perennial plants with glandular hairs. They produce alternate leaves and yellowish or violet flowers. The calyx is campanulate and the corolla funnel-shaped, slightly pendant. The plants of this genus are all poisonous but valuable for the extract of drugs used medicinally as tranquillizers and sedatives. The most important characteristic of the species illustrated is its bright golden-yellow flowers with purple throat. It is an annual or biennial species, glandular with numerous stems and leaves lobed or toothed. It establishes itself in rock fissures or on walls and ruins at low altitudes. Flowers April-June. CR.-S.E.AE.

59. ATROPA BELLA-DONA *L*.
Family: Solanaceae

A rare hairy perennial plant with a heavy smell, usually growing higher than lm. Leaves oval-acute, almost entire, alternate. Flowers in brownish-purple hues, 1 or 2 arising from the axils of the leaves. Calyx covered with down, 5 lobed at its margin. It is an extremely poisonous plant containing the alkaloid atropine and used medicinally as an antidote against the poisoning caused by mushrooms, etc., as well as to stimulate the nervous system. This plant grows in forested mountain areas. Flowers June-August. THR.- E.M.- C.M.- W.M.- EP.- THE.

60. ANTIRRHINUM MAJUS *L*. SUBSP. **TORTUOSUM**
Family: Scrophulariaceae
Modern Greek Name: Skylaki

The species included to the genus *Antirrhinum* are perennial or annual plants with entire elongated leaves and large flowers in purple, rose, yellow or white colours. Calyx with 5 lobes and corolla long tubular

strongly two-lipped. The· upper lip two-lobed and abruptly curved upwards. The lower lip is three-lobed and directed downwards. If one presses the two sides of the tube the lips open and close, strongly reminding one the mouth of a dog, hence its Greek name "skylaki," meaning small dog. The *Antirrhinum majus* is well-known everywhere in Greece as a cultivated species. The sub-species *Tortuosum* with linear leaves has been encountered by the author in such localities of the Cyclades that it is obvious that it is indigenous there. It is concluded therefore that the Cyclades and not Cicilia is the furthest point east for this subspecies to be found in spite of what has been believed to date. Flowers March-May. CY.

61. VERBASCUM BOISSIERI *(Heldr. & Sart.) O. Kuntze*

Family: Scrophulariaceae

Over 50 species of the genus *Verbascum* flourish in Greece. They are annual, biennial or perennial plants usually covered with dense down,

62a   62b

although some of them are almost smooth. They produce erect branches and usually yellow flowers arranged in a spike at the end of the stems. Calyx with 5 lobes. Corolla wide, wheel-shaped. The species illustrated favours the rocky localities of the semi-mountain and mountain zones. Basal leaves, toothed, long-stalked, lobed or pinnate. Stem leaves lanceolate, toothed. It is one of the rarest plants endemic to Greece. Flowers April-June. C.GR.

62. DIGITALIS GRANDIFLORA *Miller*
Family: Scrophulariaceae

The genus *Digitalis* includes perennial or biennial plants producing erect unbranched stems. Numerous flowers with long tubular corolla are arranged in a terminal spike. The plant illustrated is one of the six recognized species of *Digitalis* in Greek flora. It makes yellowish-white flowers up to 5cm. across, and leaves big, lanceolate, toothed with a felt of down beneath. It grows in mountain forests. Flowers June-September. THR.-E.M.-C.M.-W.M.-EP.

57

63   64

63. **DIGITALIS FERRUGINEA** *L.*

Family: Scrophulariaceae
Modern Greek Names: Korakovotano, Helidonohorto

A perennial or biennial plant producing stems usually higher than 1m. Corolla yellow with brown veins, smaller than that of the preceding species. Flowers in a very dense spike. Leaves lanceolate, slightly pubescent beneath. It grows in mountain forests. Flowers June-September. THR.-E.M.-C.M.-W.M.-EP.-THE.-C.GR.

64. **DIGITALIS LAEVIGATA** *Waldst. & Kit.*
SUBSP. **GRAECA** *(Ivanina) Werner*
Family: Scrophulariaceae

Plant resembling the preceding one with narrower and more brightly coloured flowers and leaves completely smooth. It grows in mountain forests. Flowers June-September. THR.- E.M.- C.M.- W.M.- EP.- THE.- C.GR.

58

65   66

65. LINARIA PELOPONNESIACA *Boiss. & Heldr.*
Family: Scrophulariaceae

The species of the genus *Linaria* produce flowers similar to those of *Antirrhinum,* their difference lying in the acute spur borne at the base of the former. The species illustrated grows in the mountain and alpine zones. It is a perennial with an erect unbranched stem 25-40 cm. high and leaves linear alternate. The flowers are of a yellow colour 13-20mm. long arranged in a dense terminal spike. Flowers June-August. C.M.-W.M.-EP.-THE.-C.GR.-PEL.

66. CYMBALARIA MURALIS *Gaertner*
Family: Scrophulariaceae
Modern Greek Names: Perouka, Hiliomana

Species strongly resembling *Linaria* although differing from it on account of its lobed flat heart-shaped, palmately veined leaves. It establishes itself in rock fissures, on ruins and walls at low altitudes. Flowers May-October. It is found everywhere in Greece.

59

67. GLOBULARIA STYGIA *Orph.*
Family: Globulariaceae

Four species of the genus *Globularia* grow in Greece. They produce tiny flowers of violet or bluish colour arranged in rounded heads on the end of the branches. The species illustrated is a rare plant endemic to the mountains of the Northern Peloponnese and Euboea. It is a perennial plant with woody prostrate branches, tiny leaves and small capitulums borne on very short stalks. It is a rock dweller of the alpine zone. Flowers May-July. PEL. - C.GR. (EUBOEA)

68. ACANTHUS BALCANICUS *Heywood & I.B.K. Richardson*

Family: Acanthaceae

The species included in the genus *Acanthus* are perennial plants with leaves large, pinnately lobed, most of them arising straight from the root and forming a basal rosette. The flowers are arranged in a spike. Corolla tubular, with the upper lip completely absent, in contrast to the lower one which is big, three-lobed. The species illustrated produces

a flowering stem of 40cm.-1m. high and leaves up to 70cm. across, not thorny. The flowers are of a pinkish-white or of a rosy hue. It grows in the woods or in brushwood localities of the mountain zone. Flowers May-July. THR.-E.M.-C.M.-W.M.-EP.

69. LONICERA ETRUSCA *Santi*
Family: Caprifoliaceae
Modern Greek Name: Agrio-Aghioklima

The species included to the genus *Lonicera* are perennial shrubs or clambering plants with leaves opposite, often fused at their base (perfoliate). The numerous flowers arise in terminal clusters or from the axils of the leaves. Calyx tiny. Corolla with tubular base and two-lipped margin. The lower lip is entire and the upper one is four-lobed. The species illustrated is of the most beautiful flowers growing in Greece. It grows to a shrub 3m. high with long, slender branches. Flowers up to 5cm. across, white turning to yellow-white with a rosy outer hue. Fruit fleshy, red. It frequents brushwood localities or

70   71

woods of the lower part of the mountain zone. Flowers May-June.
Ubiquitous in Greece.

70. **CENTRANTHUS RUBER** *(L) D.C.* S.SP. **SIBTHORPII** HAL.

Family: Valerianaceae
Modern Greek Name: Analatos

Kentanthuses are annual or perennial plants very similar to valerians.
Flowers small in rather dense clusters. Corolla tubular, five-lobed
with a small or big spur at its base. The species illustrated is a perennial plant which favours dry, rocky localities of the mountain and
semi-mountain zone. It produces rather numerous branches up to 1m.
high, bearing plenty of red-flowered clusters. When in bloom it is a
most ornamental plant. Flowers April-June. Ubiquitous in Greece.

71. **MORINA PERSICA** *L.*

Family: Dipsacaceae

The genus *Morina* is of Asiatic origin. The species illustrated is the
sole representative of its genus found in Europe. It is an erect

62

72   73

branched perennial plant growing up to 1.20m high. Leaves stiff, pinnate, very spiny, sessile, arise 3 or 4 together in a whorl. Flowers with corolla long, slender, tubular terminating in two opposite lobes. They are borne in dense clusters arising from the axils of the upper leaves. Blooms of an original white colour turn into purple when mature. So, there are always flowers of two different colours on the same plant. This species favours bare places of the mountain zone. Flowers June-September. THR.- E.M.- C.M.- W.M.- EP.- THE.- C.GR.- PEL.

72. KNAUTIA MAGNIFICA *Boiss. & Orph.*
Family: Dipsacaceae

The genus *Knautia* includes perennial or annual plants with opposite leaves and tiny flowers borne in heads on the tip of the branches. Corolla tubular 4- or 5-lobed. The species illustrated is one of the loveliest representatives of its genus with large, pink flower heads. Leaves lanceolate entire, hairy. It occurs in bare places of the mountain zone. Flowers June-August. THE.-C.GR.-PEL.

74

73. SCABIOSA HYMETTIA *Boiss. & Sprun*
Family: Dipsacaceae

Approximately 15 species of *Scabious* grow in Greece. They are annual or perennial plants, very similar to *Knautias*. The species illustrated is a woody-based perennial with numerous hairy branches 30-80 cm. high. Leaves narrow, lanceolate or three lobed of a greyish-green colour. Flowers in heads of lilac-pink colour. Flowers May-June. C.GR.-PEL.

74. SCABIOSA GRENATA *Cyr*.
Family: Dipsacaceae

A very variable perennial plant with numerous slender and short stems up to 25cm. high. Leaves usually pinnate. Flowers in dense heads of a pink or lilac-pink colour. It favours bare places of the mountain zone. Flowers June-August. THR.-E.M.-C.M.-W.M.-EP.-THE.-C.GR. PEL.-CR.

75

76

75. CAMPANULA PERSICIFOLIA *L*. f . *ALBA*
Family: Campanulaceae

The bell flowers are annual, biennial or perennial species with blooms in a bell, funnel or wheel shape. Calyx with 5 sepals. In Greece the genus *Campanula* includes approximately 50 species as well as many sub-species. Some of them are endemic to a single island or to a single mountain. The species illustrated is a plant of the forested mountain zone. Flowers large, up to 4cm. across usually of a bluish-lilac hue. White flowered plants are sometimes encountered, this seen usually in every *Campanula* species. Leaves narrow lanceolate. Flowers June-August. THR.- E.M.-C.M.-W.M.-EP.THE.

76. CAMPANULA RUPICOLA *Boiss*. & *Sprun*.
Family: Campanulaceae

Endemic to the mountains of Central Greece, this species establishes itself in the rock fissures of the alpine zone. Stems short, prostrate. Leaves small. One to five flowers of a bluish-violet hue are borne on each stem. Flowers July-August. C.GR.

77   78

77. **CAMPANULA OREADUM** *Boiss. & Heldr.*
Family: Campanulaceae

A dwarf plant strongly resembling the preceding one, found in the alpine zone of mount Olympus. Its name, *Oreadum,* derives from the Oread nymphs, ancient dwellers of Olympus. Flowers June-August. C.M.-THE. (MOUNT OLYMPUS).

78. **CAMPANULA ROTUNDIFOLIA** *L.* f . *ALBA*
Family: Campanulaceae

Perennial plant with slender branches and drooping flowers in bluish-violet or most rarely white colour. Leaves of the flowering stems narrow, linear in contrast to the basal leaves or to those borne on sterile shoots which are round, cordate, toothed. Hence the name of this charming bell flower which grows in the alpine zone or in the upper part of the mountain zone. Flowers June-August. E.M. - C.M.-W.M.-EP.-THE.-C.GR.-PEL.

66

79. SENECIO CORONOPIFOLIUS *Desf.*
Family: Compositae

The genus *Senecio* is well represented in Greek flora by 25 species. Flowers are usually borne in heads with yellow ray florets. The illustrated species with pinnate, almost smooth or hairy leaves grows in brushwood localities of the semi-mountain and lower mountain zone. Flowers March-April. C.GR.-PEL.-CY.-CR. It is also found elsewhere.

80. CHRYSANTHEMUM LEUCANTHEMUM *L.*
Family: Compositae

Many species of the genus *Chrysanthemum* flourish in Greece. Of course there is not an extensive relationship among them and the many cultivated varieties with double flowers which have their origin in Asiatic species. Anyway the wild chrysanthemums of Greece are rather decorative plants hence they are often seen in cultivation. The species illustrated is the ancestor of the cultivated big "ox-eye daisy."

80

It is a very variable species with leaves toothed, oblong or spathulate. The lower leaves are long-stalked and the upper ones sessile. It grows in mountain meadows and grass fields. Flowers May-June. THR. - E.M. - C.M. - W.M. - EP. THE.

81. CHRYSANTHEMUM CORYMBOSUM *L.*
Family: Compositae

Species rarely met with in Greece. It grows in mountain woods. Numerous flower-heads are borne on each branch. Ray florets white and disc-florets whitish-yellow. Leaves dissected in 7-15 lanceolate segments which are again dissected in lanceolate toothed lobes. C.M.- W.M.- EP.- THE.- C.GR.-THR.

82. CHRYSANTHEMUM SEGETUM *L.*
Family: Compositae

Species with rather big capitulums and yellow ray florets. Leaves lobed or toothed. It grows in fields and in gardens. Flowers Fe-

84

bruary-May and sometimes later on, at the beginning of autumn. EP. -
THE. - C.GR. - PEL. - CR. - CY. - N.E.AE. - S.E.AE.

83. CHRYSANTHEMUM CORONARIUM *L.*
Family: Compositae

Species similar to the preceding one with leaves more dissected and
branches generally higher. There is a variety of it with ray-florets
white and disc-florets yellow. It grows'in the meadows at low altitudes
or in the littoral zone. Flowers February-June. Everywhere in Greece
except W.M.

84. ACHILLEA ABROTANOIDES *Vis.*
Family: Compositae

The species of the genus *Achillea* are perennial, woody-based plants
with flowers borne in usually tiny capitulums. The capitulums of most
species form dense decorative clusters. The species illustrated is
sparsely districuted in Greece, growing mainly towards the northern
boundaries. The last southern point of its distribution in Europe is the

mountain Timphri of the mountain chain of Pindus. Ray-florets white. Leaves bipinnate with narrow linear segments. Flowers July-August. W.M.-EP.

85. **ACHILLEA UMBELLATA** *S. & S.*
Family: Compositae

Head flowers with white ray-florets. All the plant is covered with a silvery down. Leaves small, pinnate. Stems from 10 to 30cm. high. It grows in rocky localities of the alpine and mountain zones. THE.-C.GR.-PEL.

86. **ANTHEMIS CRETICA** *(L.) Nyman*
Family: Compositae

The species of the genus Chamomile are common plants with white or yellow ray-florets and leaves dissected in numerous linear segments. The illustrated species is a maritime plant growing on sandy littoral.

86

Ray florets absent. Flowers April-June. C.GR. -PEL.-CR.-CY.-N.E.
AE.-S.E.AE.

87. DORONICUM COLUMNAE *Tem.*
Family: Compositae

The locally-named Leopard's Bane is a large and most decorative
daisy which grows in the forests and generally on the mountains.
Leaves big. Flowers yellow. The basal leaves are long-stalked in
contrast to the sessile stem leaves. The illustrated species grows in
damp localities among the rocks of the alpine zone as well as in the
upper part of the mountain zone. Leaves reinforme-cordate, toothed.
Flowers in large capitulums, borne solitary at the end of the stem
usually higher than 50cm. Flowers June-August. THR. - E.M. - C.M.-
W.M. - EP. - THE. - C.GR. - PEL.

88. TUSSILAGO FARFARA *L.*
Family: Compositae   Modern Greek Name: Hamoleuka

This plant is the sole representative of its genus. Flower-heads up to

87

88

2.5cm. diameter. Ray-florets narrow, linear, yellow. The short red-dish shoots are overlapped by small lanceolate bracts. Leaves prostrate, **cordate, with a toothed margin. Green-coloured on the upper** surface, they are white-felted beneath. This species is valuable for its pharmaceutical properties. The leaves are popularly used as a remedy for cough and asthma. It grows in damp places of the mountain zone. Flowers February-May. Almost everywhere in Greece.

89. CENTAUREA EPIROTA *Hal.*
Family: Compositae

The genus *Centaurea* is one of the most numerous of Greek flora. It includes more than 70 species. Many of them are rare plants endemic to different mountains or islands. Head-flowers with ray-florets absent. Although, the outer disc-florets are usually sterile and longer than the inner. The illustrated species is endemic to the Balkan pen-

ninsula. Outer disc-florets in a rosy colour. Leaves greyish-green, pubescent, pinnately lobed.

90. CARLINA ACAULIS *L*. SUBSP. ALPINA *Jacq*.
Family: Compositae

The species of the genus *Carlina* have large capitulums with ray-florets absent and involucral bracts spreading, stiff, elongated. The species illustrated forms a large rosette of leaves at its base. Stems absent or very short. Leaves deeply pinnate, very spiny. Head-flowers large up to 15cm. in diameter, with silver-white bracts. This species is called the hygrometer of the mountain climbers, the bracts closing together in damp air to protect the disc, they open as soon as the sun shines again. It grows in the alpine zone of Mount Olympus and the Pindus chain. Flowers July-September. W.M.-EP.THE.

91. CARLINA ACANTHIFOLIA *All.*
Family: Compositae
Modern Greek Name: Tourta

Plant closely related to the preceding one with yellowish bracts.
Flowers July-September. It grows in the alpine zone. THR. - E.M. -
C.M. - W.M. - EP. - THE. - C.GR. - PEL.

92. INULA SERPENTINICA *Rech. & Goulimy*
Family: Compositae

The species of the genus are plants with medium-sized head-flowers.
Ray-florets, when present, are of a yellow colour. Many species have
only disc-florets. Leaves entire, more or less oblong. The illustrated
species is endemic to the mountain Vourinos of W. Macedonia. It
produces numerous branches almost 30cm. high and large capitulums
up to 5cm. across. Leaves narrow, linear-lanceolate. It was first dis-

covered by K. Goulimys in 1952. It favours stony places of the alpine zone. Flowers June-August. C.M.(VOURINOS)

93. SCILLA MESSENIACA *Boiss*.
Family: Liliaceae

Squills strongly resemble Hyacinths. Flowers usually blue or lilac with 6 perianth segments and sessile ovary. The species illustrated is endemic to the Southern Peloponnese. Flowers borne in spikes at the end of tender stems. Leaves 4-6 narrow, long, channelled. Bulb of medium size globular or egg-shaped. Flowers early in the spring from February-April. It grows in the mountain and semi-mountain zone. PEL.

94. LILIUM CHALCEDONICUM *L*.
Family: Liliaceae
Modern Greek Name: Kokkinos Krinos

The genus *Lilium* is represented in Greek flora by 5 species, all of them

being the most fascinating wild flowers. Bulbs large, scaled. Flowers big with perianth segments thick and waxy. The species illustrated is an erect branch developing from 50cm. to 1.20m. high. Leaves numerous, slightly curved, are densely borne along the whole length of the stem. Lower leaves are horizontal 5-15 cm. across and 4-5 mm. wide. The upper leaves are smaller, rather erect, covering the stem. Flowers of a bright red colour are borne from 1 to 6 on the tip of the stem. They droop downwards while the perianth segments are curled back. Species endemic to Greece favour damp places in mountain forests. Flowers June-July. W.M.-EP.-THE.-C.GR. -PEL.

95. LILIUM CANDIDUM *L.*

Family: Liliaceae
Modern Greek Names: Krinos tis Panaghias - Parthenikos Krinos
Species well known as cultivated are rarely found today as native. In Greece it can be found on a few craggy outcrops. Stem leafy from 50cm. to 1.10m high. Uppermost leaves tiny in contrast to the big basal ones. Flowers very sweet-scented, brilliant white in a lax terminal cluster of from 3 to 10 blooms in the native plants and much more

96

97

in the cultivated species. There are two varieties of this species: one producing basal leaves narrow and linear in contrast to the other which produces basal leaves wider, lanceolate, with undulate margin. Flowers May-June. C.M.- EP.- THE.- C.GR.- PEL.

96. LILIUM MARTAGON *L.S.SP.* CATANIAE
Family: Liliaceae

An erect-stemmed species growing from 50cm to 1.50 high favouring the mountain zone. Leaves elliptic-lanceolate up to 18cm. across arise 4-10 together in a whorl except the uppermost leaves which are tiny, alternate. The flowers are borne in clusters of 3-18 blooms at the end of the stems. Deep red, pink or violet darker spotted, nodding while the perianth segments are strongly recurved upwards. Flowers July-August. THR.- E.M.- C.M.- W.M.- EP.- THE.- C.GR.

97. LILIUM HELDREICHII *Freyn.*
Family: Liliaceae

This species is endemic to Mount Parnes in Attica. It strongly resem-

78

bles the *Lilium chalcedonicum*. A single flower is borne at the end of the stem while the basal leaves are wider than those of the *Lilium chalcedonicum* and the uppermost leaves are tiny. It is rather, a sub-species. Flowers June-July. C.GR. (PARNES)

98. FRITILLARIA GRAECA *Boiss. & Sprun.*
Family: Liliaceae

The flowers of the genus *Fritillaria* are closely related to tulips although they are not as fascinating as the latter. Brown and green are the dominating colours of their perianth. Another difference from tulips is that their flowers are always nodding downwards or spreading. The species illustrated grows in the mountain zone. It has one to two flowers and leaves oblong incurved. It favours bare rocky places and flowers March-May. EP.-THE.-C.GR.-PEL.

99. URGINEA MARITIMA *(L.) Baker*
Family: Liliaceae   Modern Greek Name: Skylokremida

The species illustrated growing up to 1m. in height is the sole rep-

resentative of the genus in Greek flora. Bulb very large up to 15cm. across. Leaves lanceolate up to 30 cm. length appearing only after flowering, by the end of autumn. Flowers white, tiny, borne in long spikes at the end of strong stems appear from August-October. It grows in stony places and brushwood localities of low altitude. E.M. C.M.-EP.-THE.-C.GR.-CR.-CY.N.E.AE.-S.E.AE.

100. CONVALLARIA MAJALIS *L.*
Family: Liliaceae
Modern Greek Name: Péka

This charming plant, the common Muguet, well known in Europe where it is widely cultivated, is a perennial with creeping rhizome which continually gives rise to new stems. Flowers little, pendent, bellshaped, pure white are borne 4-9 in one-sided clusters along a tender stem. Leaves usually 2, very big, lanceolate with strong parallel nerves. It favours fertile soils and damp, cool localities of the mountain zone. Flowers April-June. THR. - E.M. - C.M. - W.M. - EP. - THE. - C.GR. - PEL.

101. ALLIUM SPHAEROCEPHALUM *L.*
Family: Liliaceae

The genus *Allium* well represented in Greek flora by over 40 species, includes plants known as wild onions and wild garlics which smell strongly of onion. Flowers numerous, borne in leafless terminal umbels. Leaves basal or arising from the lower part of the stem, narrow, strap-like, hollowed or grooved above. The illustrated species produces flowers purple with stamens longer than the perianth segments, borne on erect stems approximately 80cm. high. It grows in the mountain zone or in some low altitude areas. Flowers June-August. Ubiquitous in Greece.

102. SMILAX ASPERA *L.*
Family: Liliaceae
Modern Greek Names: Arkoudovatos, Ailaki.

This strange plant has no close relationship to the other species of the family *Liliaceae*. It is a climbing evergreen plant with branches woody, long, spiny. Leaves alternate, cordate to arrow-shaped, leath-

103

ery. Flowers tiny, yellowish green borne numerous in small bouquets. Smilax is one-sexed plant. Female flowers are borne on different plants from those bearing male flowers. It grows in bushy places of the semi-mountain zone or in low-altitude localities. Flowers in spring and its fruit ripens from September-November. Ubiquitous in Greece.

103. ORNITHOGALUM NANUM *S. & S.*
Family: Liliaceae

The genus *Ornithogalum* includes almost a dozen species of Greek flora which unfortunately have not been completely studied yet. Flowers white with 6 perianth segments. They are borne numerous on an elongated or flat-topped terminal spike. The species illustrated is a little plant with short stems up to 10cm. high and leaves very narrow, spreading. It grows in bushy places or bare localities of the semi-mountain zone or at low altitudes. Flowers April-May. Everywhere in Greece.

104   105

104. TULIPA HAGERI *Heldr*.
Family: Liliaceae

Tulips are of the most fascinating plants of Greek flora. Their brightly coloured flowers have always drawn the attention of people and their repeated picking has put the plant in danger of disappearance. Many localities where tulips were thriving are now bare of this plant. Flowers with 6 perianth segments arise usually solitary or rarely two at the end of the stem. Leaves usually oblong arise from the lowest part of the stem. The species illustrated produces flowers approximately 4cm. length, always in bright red colour, and stamens almost black. Bulbs small with smooth surface. Leaves linear, grooved. It grows in bare meadows of the mountain zone, flowers April-May. C.GR., PEL.-CR.-N.E.AE. It can be found in other regions as well.

105. TULIPA SAXATILIS *Sieb*.
Family: Liliaceae

Marvellous species, endemic to Crete where it decorates the

meadows of the mountain zone with its lovely flowers. Perianth segments of a rosy-violet colour with a yellow blotch at their base, up to 5cm. across. Leaves usually 3, narrow, lanceolate. Each plant gives rise to one or two blooms. Flowers March-May. CR.

106. TULIPA GOULIMYI Sealy & Turrill
Family: Liliaceae

Rare species of tulip, endemic to the Southern Peloponnese and to the island of Kythira. It is closely related to *Tulipa hageri,* their difference lying in the greater number of leaves produced by the former (usually 6) and in its large and very hairy bulb. It grows in fields and bushy localities of low altitude or in the semi-mountain zone. Flowers March-April. PEL.

107. MERENDERA ATTICA Boiss.
Family: Liliaceae

Perennial plants with egg-shaped corm are included to the genus

Merendera. Flowers strongly resemble Autumn Crocus are readily distinguished by the perianth segments dissected almost up to the base of the very long tube. The species illustrated grows in brushwood localities of low altitude. Flowers pale pink, stalkless, arising straight from the corm encircled by 3-4 narrow leaves. Flowers October-November C.GR.-PEL.

108. COLCHICUM CATACUZENIUM *Heldr*.
Family: Liliaceae

This plant strongly resembles the other Autumn Crocus *(Colchicum)*, nevertheless it flowers in spring. Leaves usually three. Flowers 2-3 pinkish or white. Bulb egg-shaped coated with a brownish tunic. It grows on the barren meadows of the alpine zone. Flowers February-May.C.M.-THE.-PEL. Its presence is possible to other regions as well.

109. **COLCHICUM BOWLESIANUM** *B. L. Burtt*
Family: Liliaceae

A large group of different autumn Crocuses containing 27 species, many of which are endemic to the Greek peninsula. A corm or more seldom a rhizome is borne at their root. Flowers arise in the autumn straight from the corm. Perianth segments 6 fused below to a very long tube. Stigmas 3 filiformed. Leaves appear with the flowers or in the next spring. The species illustrated, endemic to Greece, is one of the loveliest representatives of the genus. Petals dark spotted, 5.5 cm. across. Leaves usually 9, narrow and linear up to 25 cm. long. Flowers appear in the autumn during the months September and October while the leaves appear the next spring. It grows in bare localities of the mountain zone. C.M.-W.M.

110. **COLCHICUM VARIEGATUM** *L.*
Family: Liliaceae

Plant closely related to the preceding one, it differs from it on account

of its slightly smaller flowers. Leaves 2-4 lanceolate up to 15cm. in length. It grows in the woods of the mountain zone. Flowers September-October. C.GR.-PEL.-S.E.AE.-CY.-CR.

111a. COLCHICUM MAKROPHYLLUM B. L. Burtt
111b. *Family: Liliaceae*

This rare plant endemic to Greece is found confined to the islands of Crete and Rhodes. Its flowers are similar to those of the preceding species while its leaves, appearing in the spring, are much longer, up to 35cm. across and 14cm. wide. It grows in the semi-mountain and mountain zones. Flowers September-October. CR.-S.E.AE.

112. COLCHICUM PARNASSICUM *Sart., Orph., & Heldr.*
Family: Liliaceae
Modern Greek Name: Volhiko

Endemic to Greece, this charming species has a long tubed perianth terminating in pink or almost white segments with dark spots absent,

3.5cm. long. Corm large of a dark brown colour. Leaves 4-5 oblong 4.5cm. wide. It grows on bare places of the mountain zone. Flowers August-September. THE.-C.GR.-PEL.

113. **COLCHICUM BALANSAE** *Planch*.
Family: Liliaceae

Plant of Asiatic origin, found growing on Rhodes as well. It is closely related to the preceding one. Nevertheless, it produces white flowers, leaves bigger and corm with very long tube. Flowers September-October. S.E.AE. (RHODES)

114. **COLCHICUM KOCHII** *Parl*.
Family: Liliaceae

Leaves rather small and narrow up to 1cm. wide. Corm small. Flowers pale pink with perianth segments narrow. It grows on bare lands of the mountain and semi-mountain zone. Flowers September-October. C.M.- W.M.- EP.

114

115

115. GALANTHUS REGINAE OLGAE *Orph.*
Family: Amaryllidaceae
Modern Greek Name: Skoularikia

The genus *Galanthis* is easily distinguished from the remaining genera of the family *Amaryllidaceae* on account of the strange shape of its flowers. Their 3 inner perianth segments are much shorter than the 3 outer ones. Leaves always two, strap-shaped and flowers solitary, nodding, pure white, are also characteristic features of this genus. The illustrated species is a rare plant endemic to the mountain zone of Mount Taygettus. It is closely related to *Galanthus nivalis* well-known in Europe. It flourishes November-December, the leaves appearing later. PEL.

116. NARCISSUS POETICUS *L.* SUBSP. RADIIFLORUS *Burh.*
Family: Amarillidaceae
Modern Greek Names. Zumpuki, Narkissos

Perennial plants with egg-shaped bulbs are included to this genus.

89

116

117

Leaves strap-shaped arise straight from the base in two rows. Flowers sweet-scented with long tube and corona. Ovary inferior. A spathe encircles the buds borne at the end of a stem. Flowering stem is hollow, leafless, slightly wide. *Narkissus poeticus* is a widely distributed species of the mountain and alpine zone. It displays numerous sub-species two of which are found growing in Greece. The species illustrated, in contrast to the local one, makes smaller flowers with perianth segments narrower. Leaves smaller and narrower as well. The sub-species *radiiflorus* frequents drier and stony localities. Flowers April-May. THR.-E.M.-C.M.-W.M.-C. GR. It can be found in other regions as well.

117. NARCISSUS TAZETTA *L.S.SP.* LACTACOLOR (HAW.) BAKER

Family: Amaryllidaceae
Modern Greek Name. Zampaki, Manoussaki

Flowers 2-4cm. across, borne numerous on each stem, are much smaller than those of the preceding species. It is distinguished in many

sub-species on the basis of the size and the colour of its flowers as well as on other secondary characteristics. Its usual colour is the cream-white with yellow corona. It grows in the fields of low altitude favouring damp localities. Flowers January-March. THE. - C.GR. - PEL. - CY. - CR. - N.E.AE. - S.E.AE.

118. STERNBERGIA LUTEA *(L.) Sprengel*
Family: Amaryllidaceae
Modern Greek Names: Krinaki, Agriokrinos

Flowers yellow with a short tube and ovary inferior are borne at first in a spathe solitary or two at the end of a short stem. Leaves strap-shaped grow straight from the egg-shaped bulb. The species illustrated produces a stem up to 30cm. high and flowers 5cm. across. Leaves appear with the flowers. It grows in stony localities of the semi-mountain and mountain zones. Flowers September-October. C.GR.- PEL. It can occur in other localities as well.

119

119. PANCRATIUM MARITIMUM *L*.

Family: Amaryllidaceae   Modern Greek Name: Krinos tis Thalassas

This plant is the sole representative of its genus found in Greece. Flowers pure white, large with long tube and perianth segments slender, strap-shaped. They are borne in an umbel on a stout, high, leafless stalk. The characteristic feature of the genus is the large trumpet-shaped corona terminating in twelve teeth which alternate with 6 stamens. Leaves long, strap-shaped, make their appearance soon after the flowering. The bulb is very large, up to 10cm. in diameter. The marvellous sweet-scented flowers decorate sandy littorals from August-September. Unfortunately the tourist development of the coasts has been followed by the uncontrolled picking of these flowers. Hence the great reduction in number of these plants. Everywhere in Greece except W.M.

120. IRIS GERMANICA *L*.

Family: Iridaceae   Modern Greek Names: Krinos-Agriokrinos

Perennial plants with a bulb or a rhizome at their root are included in

120

121

this genus. Flowers large·with 6 perianth segments arranged in two whorls. The outer 3 segments, or falls, spread or curve downwards while the inner 3 segments, or standards, are erect. Stamens three, covered by the three strange stigmas which are wide and big. The species illustrated is one of the most enchanting in Greek flora. Rhizome perennial. Leaves sword-shaped or sickle-shaped. Flowers displaying every shade of violet colour are large, up to 10cm. across. Flourishes April-June. It may be encountered as a native or as a cultivated plant almost everywhere in Greece. EP.

121. IRIS FLORENTINA L.
Family: Iridaceae
Modern Greek Names: Krinos, Aspros Krinos

Species strongly resembling the preceding one. It produces white flowers. It is a common plant, both native and cultivated. It grows in gardens and fields at low altitudes. Flowers March-April. Ubiquitous in Greece.

93

122. IRIS CRETICA *Janka (IRIS INGUICULARIS SUBSP.* CRETENSIS)
Family: Iridaceae

Perennial plant bearing a rhizome at its root. Leaves narrow, elongated. Flowers violet. It grows in stony localities of the mountain, semi-mountain and low altitude zones. Flowers January-March. THE.-C.GR.-PEL.-CY.-CR.-S.E.AE.

123. IRIS PUMILA *L.* SUBSP. **ATTICA** *Boiss. & Heldr.*
Family: Iridaceae

Dwarf plant with a creeping rhizome and leaves small sword-shaped or sickle-shaped. Flowers rather large displaying a variety of colours from white and dull yellow to rich purple. It grows in stony localities of the mountain zone or at low altitudes. Flowers March-May. THE.-C.GR.-PEL.

124. IRIS SISYRINCHIUM *L.*
Family: Iridaceae   Modern Greek Name: Afti tou Lagou

Plant with an egg-shaped corm enclosed in a fibrous coat. Leaves

124

125

narrow, channelled. Flowers blue or bluish-violet. It grows in the
littoral zone or in localities at low altitudes. Flowers March-May.
THR. - E.M. - C.M. - THE. - C.GR. - PEL. - CY. - CR. - N.E.AE. -
S.E.AE.

125. GLADIOLUS ILLYRICUS *Koch*
Family: Iridaceae

The genus *Gladiolus* is represented in Greek flora by four species. All
of them produce a small globular or egg-shaped corm and leaves
narrow, elongated sword-shaped. Flowers smaller than those of the
cultivated species in a violet-purple or in a pink colour are borne on
one-sided spikes along the stems. The species illustrated grows up to
50cm. high. Leaves narrow 9mm. wide. Flowers from three to nine on
each plant with the uppermost perianth segment longer and narrower
than the lateral ones. It grows amidst crops and in meadows of the
mountain and semi-mountain zones. Flowers May-June. THR.-
E.M.-C.M.-W.M.-EP.-THE. Its presence is possible in other regions
as well.

95

126

126. CROCUS OLIVIERII *Day*
Family: Iridaceae

The genus *Crocus* includes almost 20 species of Greek flora. Some of them flower during the spring while others flower during the autumn. They have a small corm covered with fibres. Leaves slender, linear with central band above. Perianth segments 6, stamens 3. Style long with 3 stigmas which are big, flattening, toothed or further divided into many segments. The illustrated species grows early in the spring from March to May in bare meadows of the mountain zone. Leaves 4-5 appear at the same time as the flowers. Anthers and stigmas in a bright yellow colour as well as the rest of the flower. THR.- E.M.- C.M.- W.M.- EP.- THE.- C.GR.- PEL.

127. CROCUS CANCELLATUS *Herb.*
Family: Iridaceae

It is an autumn flowering plant with pale violet or white coloured blooms. Perianth with long tube. Leaves 3-4, very narrow, appear

96

127   128

after the flowers. Corm globular encircled by a network of fibres. It grows in the lowest part of the mountain zone. Flowers September-October. W.M.-EP.-THE.-C.GR.-PEL.-CY.-CR.-S.E.AE. Its presence is possible in other regions as well.

128. CROCUS LAEVIGATUS *Ch. & B.*
Family: Iridaceae

This charming plant grows in bare localities of the mountain and semi-mountain zones. Leaves 3-4 appearing with the flowers. Perianth segments 2-2.5cm. across in a white or pale violet colour with three dark veins at their base. Tube with yellow throat grows above the ground. Flowers November-January. THE.- C.GR.- PEL.- CR.

129. CROCUS CARTWRIGHTIANUS *Herb.*
Family: Iridaceae

Plant with flowers white or violet with strong dark veins. Anthers

97

129

yellow. Stigmas very long projecting and pendent out of the corolla in a bright orange or red colour. Leaves 6-10 appear the same time with the flowers. It grows in ravines and brushwood localities of low altitude. Flowers early in autumn from September till October. C.GR.-CY.CR.-S.E.AE. PEL.

130. CROCUS SIEBERI *J. Gay.* VAR. ATTICUS *Boiss & Orph.*
Family: Iridaceae

A spring flowering species of the mountain zone. Leaves 3-5. Flowers in various violet shades with tube yellow and smooth. Flowers March-April. THE.-C.GR.-PEL. It can occur in other regions as well.

131. ANACAMPTIS PYRAMIDALIS *(L.) L.C.M. Richard*
Family: Orchidaceae

This species is the sole representative of the genus *Anacamptis*. Two small egg-shaped tubers produced at its root give rise to an unbranched erect stem 20-60cm. in height. Leaves narrow, lineal-lanceolate.

130   131

Flowers very similar to orchids are borne in beautiful clusters at the end of the stem. Spur very long. Lip deeply three-lobed. This species withstands any climate condition and grows in any place from the maritime brushwood localities up to the alpine zone. Flowers May-July. Ubiquitous in Greece.

132. ORCHIS ITALICA *Poiret*
Family: Orchidaceae
Modern Greek Name: Salépi

Perennial plants with two charactetistic tubers at the base of their shoot are included in the genus *Orchis*. Tubers when dried and ground yield a floury substance which after being boiled makes the soothing drink "Salepi." Petals six, the outer three usually equal, clongated, while the three inner differ very much. Two of them are elongated while the lowest is conspicuously bigger and dissected in three parts or lobes. This lowest petal is called a lip and bears a long spur backwards. The shape, the colour and the size of the lip are most important factors for

99

132

133

the identification of each species. The species illustrated has 5 petals coming together in a helmet with very long three-lobed lip. The median lobe is dissected in linear segments while the lateral ones are long, linear. The whole flower looks like the body of a little man. It grows in brushwood and stony localities of the mountain and semi-mountain zones. Flowers April-May. THE.-C.GR.-PEL.-CY. Its presence is possible in other regions as well.

133. DACTYLORHIZA SAMBUCINA *(L.) Soo*
Family: Orchidaceae

The species included in the genus *Dactylorhiza* are strongly related to Orchis, their difference lying in the shape of the tubers. The tubers of Dactylorhiza have finger-like projections directed downwards in contrast to the tubers of the Orchis which are entire. The species illustrated has flowers covering a range of colours from purple to yellow. It grows in the meadows of the mountain and alpine zones. Flowers April-June. THR.-E.M.-C.M.-W.M. EP.-THE.-C.GR.-PEL.

134

135

134. **OPHRYS FUSCA** *Link*
Family: Orchidaceae

The genus *Ophrys* has the same general features as those of Orchis, their difference lying in the absence of a flower-spur. The species illustrated displays great variety. Its main characteristic is the elongated, almost black velvet lip. It grows at low altitudes or in the semi-mountain zone. Flowers February-May. Almost everywhere in Greece.

135. **OPHRYS TENTHREDINIFERA** *Willd*
Family: Orchidaceae
Modern Greek Names: Kori, Mélissa

It is a lovely species with lip dark coloured at its base and lighter coloured at its tip. The remaining petals are of a rosy hue. Short, 10-30cm. high. It grows in brushwood localities at low-altitudes. Flowers March-May. C.GR.- PEL.- CV.- CR.- N.E.AE. S.E.AE. Its presence is possible in other regions as well.

101

A. ROSA PENDULINA *L.*

A very small shrub widespread in the Alps and other European mountains. In Greece, however, it is rare, and found only in the mountain and alpine zones. One of its distinguishing features is the lack of thorns on its branches. The plant blooms from June until September.

103

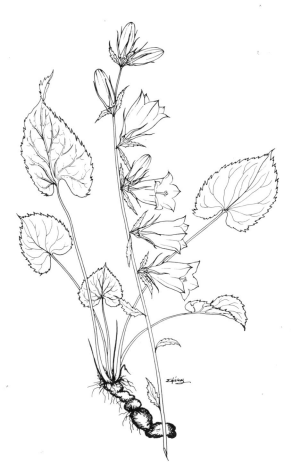

B. SYMPHYANDRA CRETICA *A. DE CANDOL*
This species, closely related to Campanula, is endemic to Greece and
occurs in three sub-species: one at Samothrace, one in the Sporhades,
one on Crete. Flowers from July until August.

104

C. ROSA CANINA L.

Common to the mountain zone of Greece, this tall shrub grows from 1 to 5 metres in height and is distinguished by its big sickle-shaped thorns and its smooth fruit. Blooms from April to June.

D. ADONIS AESTIVALIS *L.*
An attractive plant common to almost every part of Greece. Its reddish flowers appear from April until June.

E. PRIMULA ELATIOR *(L.) HILL*
Widespread in European forests, in Greece this plant is found exclusively in the mountain zone. Flowers from March to May.

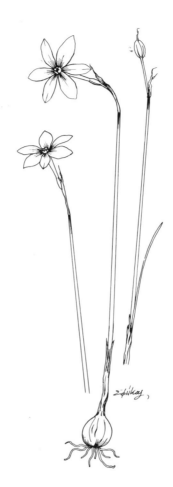

F. NARCISSUS SEROTINUS *L.*

This plant favours the lowland zone where it grows amidst *maquis* (brushwood), flowering from September to October. A single flower is produced from every bulb and a slender leaf sometimes grows from the stem of the flower.

G. CAMPANULA GLOMERATA *L.*

Confined to the mountain zone, this is among the most beautiful Campanula species in Greece. Flowers from June to August.

H. PUNICA GRANATUM *L.*

Endemic to Greece since ancient times, this plant of unknown origin is often seen in cultivation. The flowers appear in spring and are followed by edible fruit.

I. TULIPA BOEOTICA *BOISS. & HELDR.*
Endemic to Greece, where it is found in fields and grasslands at low altitudes. Its attractive red flowers appear from March until May.

J. CROCUS FLEISCHERI *J. GAY*
   A rare plant of Asia Minor also met with on the Greek islands of Samos and Rhodes. Flowers from December to February.

112

K. CROCUS GOULIMYI *TURR.*

A rare plant endemic to the *maquis* (brushwood) localities of the Southern Peloponnese. It is distinctive for its exceedingly long tube of flowers which blossom from October until November.

113

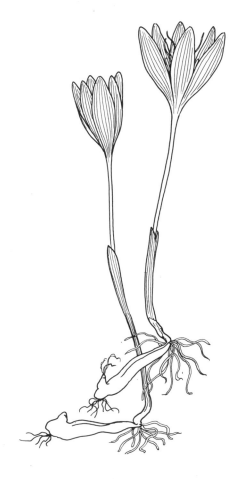

L. COLCHICUM BOISSIERI *ORPH.*

Endemic to Greece where it is found, though it is rare, in the forests of the mountain zone. In contrast with the other Colchics, a rhizome rather than a bulb appears at its root. It is probable that C. Boissieri, in common with the smaller C. Psaridis, is the ancestor of the species Colchicum.

M. **STERNBERGIA SICULA** *TEN.*

Widespread in rocky areas at low altitudes. The flowers bloom from September to November, while the leaves begin growing as soon as the flowering season is over.

N. EBENUS CRETICA L.

Endemic to the island of Crete where it is found in rocky localities, this is one of the most captivating examples of Greek flora. Its pink or purple flowers bloom from March to July.

O. TULIPA AUSTRALIS *LINK.*

Rocky localities within the mountain zone are favoured by this delicate tulip. It usually produces 2 leaves, and flowers no more than 4 cm in length.

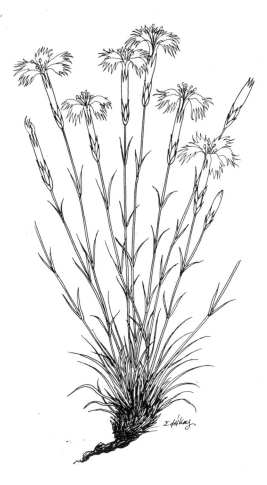

P. DIANTHUS CRINITUS *SMITH.*
This is an extremely rare Asiatic plant which also grows on the island of Rhodes, the furthest point to the west that it is found. Its flowers are white and bloom from March to May.

INDEX

INDEX

INDEX

INDEX

BIBLIOGRAPHY

Flora Europea
Flora of Turkey   P.H. Davis
Flowers of Europe   Oleg Polunin
Flowers of the Mediterranean Oleg Polunin - Athony Huxley
Votanikon Phytologikon
                                         D. Kavvadas
Wild Flowers   M. Skytte Christiansen
Wild Flowers of Europe   Paul Hamlyn

Wild flowers of Greece

ISBN 960 226 061 0

21183503

EFSTATHIADIS
GROUP

9 789602 260616

Cheers! B.J. (note the orange juice) at a cricket lunch with Jim Laker and Frank Butler, Sports Editor of the *News of the World*.

Two old codgers . . . the Oval 1977. B.J. with his old Australian broadcasting mate Alan McGilvray.

'Talk About! B.J. with Sound Supervisor Cedric Johnson and producer Roger Macdonald, follows the Queen and the Lord Mayor, Sir Robin Gillett on the walkabout from St Paul's to Guildhall on Jubilee Day, 7 June 1977.
(Copyright Keystone Press Agency Ltd)

The portrait looks down on Pauline, Mini and B. J. (Copyright *Marylebone Mercury*)

Sixty-five years on. B. J. returns to his birthplace to open the Little Berkhamsted cricket pavilion with Barbara Cartland, introduced by Lord Orr-Ewing.
(Copyright Pauline Johnston)

The family say 'Cheese!' (left to right) Andrew, Barry, Pauline, Joanna, B.J., Clare and Ian. New Year 1978.

(and golf) ball vast distances, his most famous hit being the one which cleared the Frank Woolley Stand at Canterbury. But at Eton he suffered from the terrible pitches on which he had to play. So did my friend William Douglas-Home who was prompted to write a letter once to the *Eton College Chronicle*. In one of their recent reports of a first XI match they had said that the Eton captain had failed yet again and had obviously struck a bad patch. 'Tell him to come and play on some of our Middle Club pitches, and he'll strike a few more!' wrote William.

Charles of course rose to great heights culminating with his very successful Governor-Generalship of New Zealand. But to his immense satisfaction he ultimately became a better and more successful cricketer than most of those who had got their XI at Eton. As captain of Worcestershire in the late thirties he brought a gaiety and sense of enjoyment into county cricket which is so sadly lacking today. In spite of the many high offices he held, at Court and in the City, he was the least pompous of men and told many stories against himself.

Once, when captaining Worcestershire against Gloucestershire he had to go into bat against Charlie Parker on a sticky wicket. Off his first ball he was missed at slip by Hammond of all people – a sharp low chance to his right hand. The second ball hit the stumps without removing the bails. The third hit him on the pads and he survived a confident appeal for LBW. The fourth, believe it or not, went to Hammond's left hand and again was dropped. The fifth mercifully bowled him neck and crop. As he made his way back to the pavilion somewhat embarrassed he passed Charlie Barnett who was fielding at third man. 'Bad luck, skipper,' Charlie said. 'You were never quite in!'

Charles always used to say that his idea of heaven was to bat against his own bowling. I wouldn't know whether he will actually be able to play cricket in heaven, but I am willing to bet that even if he isn't, he'll be holding the floor, with his stories, and making them all laugh up there!

At the end of October for the first time in my life I was asked to give the address at a memorial service. It was for a unique and remarkable character called Buns Cartwright, who for forty years had been secretary of the Eton Ramblers, and their president for another twenty-one. I had known him since the early thirties when I first played for the Ramblers, and had been his friend ever since. I approached this daunting task with great trepidation because he had so many friends and acquaintances in every walk of life. They knew all about him – his many good points and the inevitable few which were not so good, which we all have.

He was an eccentric, especially in his dress, which was usually a blue pin-stripe suit with carnation and blue plimsolls, topped with a brown cap, or one of his many sombreros with the Rambler ribbon around it. He was one of a dying breed – man about town, clubman, sportsman and *bon viveur*. He never owned nor drove a car but could be seen at nearly every big sporting occasion, with cricket, tennis, golf and racing taking priority. He was irascible, gruff, critical but underneath it all was a kind man with a sharp wit and keen sense of humour. He was also an inveterate gambler and when my wife Pauline went to see him in hospital he even offered her odds of 7–4 against his own recovery.

It was obviously no good giving a solemn oration full of false praise and sentiment about such a character. So I decide to recall him as we all knew him and included one or two of the more respectable stories about him. The Guards Chapel was absolutely packed and it was the first time I had ever heard laughs at a Memorial Service. But I am certain that it was what he would have wanted, and in a strange way showed our love and friendship for him, and our gratitude for all he had done for us. But it is not a task which I want to do again.

In the New Year 1977 we went down to Windsor to the delightful Theatre Royal which is run so beautifully and efficiently by John Counsell. We went to see a new play by William Douglas-Home, one of three which eventually ran simultaneously in the West End. It was called *In the Red* and was all about a popular playwright who lived entirely on a vast overdraft at his bank – I wonder where William got all the necessary background information! I thought the play very funny and so did all the provincial audiences. But it failed when it came to London, possibly because the audiences looked on it as a fantasy, just not believing that anyone could really live like that.

There were some very good jokes in *In the Red* and I suggested another to William – I am not sure whether he put it in or not. It was the old one of the client who was being persistently pressed by his bank manager to pay off his overdraft. The client finally got fed up. 'You remember, two years ago, when I was in credit with you for five hundred pounds?' he asked the bank manager. 'Yes, I do,' replied the bank manager grudgingly. 'Well,' said the client, 'I didn't go on badgering you to pay *me* back, did I?'

Incidentally, I must try that out on *my* bank manager some time. The trouble is you have to be in credit first!

It was in February 1977 that I suffered a great disappointment. Len Maddocks – the old Australian wicket-keeper and manager of their 1977 team to England – rang me from Australia to ask me to go out there for the Centenary Test at Melbourne in March. He wanted me to make a speech at the champagne breakfast which was going to take place on the first morning of the match before play started. I couldn't really believe it. Many of my cricketing friends were already booked to go and here I was being asked to fly 13,000 miles just to make a speech. I dearly wanted to go, but, alas, the invitation came too late. I was already committed for *Down Your Way*, at least four dinners and the Boat Race, and could not cancel them all at such short notice.

I shall always be sorry that I was not able to be there at such a unique occasion – unique, because when again will there ever be such a gathering of past and present Test players spanning nearly sixty years of English and Australian Test cricket. What a fabulous opportunity it was for old and young players to meet and swop experiences. Everyone who went there was full of praise for the wonderful hospitality and organisation. Nothing seems to have gone wrong. Even the weather and the cricket matched the occasion. The gods must indeed have been on the side of the Australian organisers. Fancy arranging for the Queen to visit the match on the *fifth day* and to find that when she arrived the game was building up to a dramatic climax. The betting must have been that the match would have already finished or be heading for a dull draw. And to think that England lost by 45 runs – exactly the same margin by which they had lost that first Test in 1877. And what about Randall's brilliant and cheeky innings of 174? You can see why I was so disappointed – which reminds me of the difference between disappointment and despair. Disappointment is the first time you discover you can't do it twice. Despair is the second time you discover you can't do it once!

Jubilee Day 7 June 1977

Over the past thirty-two years I have been extremely lucky in having a grandstand seat for all the big Royal occasions during that time – and incidentally I have always been *outside* somewhere, never *inside*. First in 1947 I was on the Victoria Memorial outside Buckingham Palace for the wedding of Princess Elizabeth and Prince Philip. Then in 1952 it was Hyde Park corner for TV for King George VI's funeral, and again for TV in Hyde Park for the Coronation procession in 1953. Next I was with the TV cameras outside the garden of No. 10 Downing Street on Horse Guards Parade to describe Princess Margaret's wedding procession and, finally, thirteen years later I was commentating for radio by the Citadel on the corner of Horse Guards for Princess Anne's wedding. On all these occasions I have had superb close-up views of all the processions as they passed by, but never in my wildest dreams did I ever imagine that I would take part in one.

It happened on Jubilee Day when I was covering part of the celebrations for radio. My first position which I reached by 8 am was on Queen Anne's statue outside the steps of St Paul's Cathedral leading up to the west door. Scaffolding and a platform had been placed round the statue so that we could see right down Ludgate Hill to Ludgate Circus or behind us up the twenty-eight steps into the Cathedral itself as the congregation took their seats.

It was cool, windy and cloudy but not actually raining as we made our way through the crowds already five or six deep behind the barriers. Many had been there all night and we actually found a vicar from the Isle of Wight who, with his family, had been on the pavement since midnight on the

Sunday. Everyone was in tremendous spirits and already at this early hour there was plenty for them to watch with troops marching along the route to take up their positions. A dustman at the back of a cart which had been sprinkling sand on the wet streets acknowledged the cheers of the crowd in the Queen's best manner. There were wolf whistles from the teenage girls as some Scottish soldiers marched by, their kilts being blown up by the wind. I'm sure that at least some of the crowd now know the answer to that eternal question: 'Do they?' or 'Don't they?' An important-looking official in top hat and tails had a rather mincing gait and was greeted with cries of 'Are you free, Mr Humphries?' Some of the crowd kept singing *For She's a Jolly Good Sovereign* and others shouted the odds when a large picture hat blew off the head of a stately dowager and was pursued down Ludgate Hill by her top-hatted escort.

Between 9.30 and 10.30 am the official guests arrived, some like the Speaker and Lord Mayor in their own coaches. Then came the carriage processions with their escorts and the crowds were really getting their reward for their long wait. Princess Anne and Captain Mark Phillips came first, then the Queen Mother and her two grandsons Prince Andrew and Prince Edward. And what a cheer she got! As usual she looked superb.

And then the big moment with the clip-clop of the House-hold Cavalry coming slowly up the hill, followed by the eight Windsor Greys pulling the four-ton newly gilded Golden Coach with the Queen and the Duke of Edinburgh, waving to the crowds as the band of the Honourable Artillery Company played the National Anthem. I got a perfect view as the coach wheeled slowly round in front of the steps, and there was an anxious moment as one of the greys slipped and took fright.

Two days later I was in Goring on Thames for a *Down Your Way* and interviewed the Queen's saddler who has a saddle and harness shop there. He told me he had been up at 4 am in the Royal Mews preparing and checking all the harness. He revealed something which I don't think anyone saw – I certainly didn't and I was only a few feet away. As the Golden Coach was swinging round to the right, the off-side back wheel knocked against one of the bollards outside the Cathedral. It not only shook the coach, but the wheel might well have come off. I expect the Queen and the Duke must have realised something had gone wrong when they felt the bump.

I was able to watch the Royal party greeted on the steps by the Archbishop of Canterbury and the Lord Mayor, and then see them disappear into the brilliantly lit interior of St Paul's before the big west doors were closed. The service was relayed to the crowds outside and I was able to listen to it from my perch on Queen Anne's statue.

At the end of the service the Royal party came down the steps and then the Queen and Duke of Edinburgh, accompanied only by the Lord and Lady Mayoress, started what was to be the Queen's happiest and most successful of all her many walk-abouts. It was certainly seen by more people than all the others put together because of the worldwide TV coverage of Jubilee Day.

I said just now that the Queen was accompanied by the Lord Mayor and Lady Mayoress. That's not quite true. By some means the BBC Radio had been given permission for me to follow closely behind the Queen with a small mobile transmitter. I just couldn't believe my luck, though I felt some slight trepidation at having to walk through so many thousands of cheering people. The Queen was used to it, but I definitely wasn't! Anyway, with my producer, Roger MacDonald, and our engineer, Cedric Johnson, we set off. We followed just a few yards behind the Queen and I gave the best commentary I could manage as I walked along. It was a really fantastic experience. The Queen stopped every few yards to talk to the crowd, and accepted dozens of little posies from small children all along the route. The Lord Mayor Sir Robin Gillett did his best to act as a carrier bag!

Many people thrust their hands out for the Queen to shake, but I only saw her shake hands with one person – an old grey-haired soldier with a cluster of medals on his chest, and as she left him, there were tears pouring down his cheeks. A magnificent moment for him. We soon got a long way ahead of the Duke, who as usual had plenty to say to everyone and cracked jokes which drew roars of laughter from the crowds. We walked through the gardens on the north side of St Paul's, then out into Cheapside through the lines of spectators. The noise was deafening and as you can imagine I got quite a bit of friendly barracking from the crowd. They must have been surprised to see me coming *Down Their Way*, and amazed that I was following so closely behind the Queen apparently talking to myself.

I stopped and asked quite a few of them what the Queen had said to them and generally it seemed to be: 'Where do you come from?' and 'How long have you been waiting?' and so on. It was noticeable that when the Queen stopped to talk to someone, the cheering stopped, only to be renewed as soon as she went on her way. The Duke occasionally caught up with us and even remarked that I looked like a man from space with my headphones and the aerial on our mobile transmitter.

When we turned into the narrow King Street with high buildings on either side the noise became deafening. I was getting a bit cocky by now and so far forgot myself as to ask the Duke whether he would say something to the listeners over my microphone. With a cheerful grin he shouted, 'I can't hear myself speak!'

We finally reached the Guildhall and the walk had taken about half an hour. Even the Queen, so used to these sorts of demonstrations of love and loyalty, must have been over-whelmed by the tremendous reception she received from every-one along the route. I certainly will never forget it and it was definitely one of the highlights of my broadcasting career. I was naturally very pleased that the BBC used some of my commentary on a band of the BBC Jubilee Commemorative Record of the broadcasts of the Silver Jubilee Events, which they published in aid of the Queen's Jubilee Fund.

The day before my sixty-fifth birthday – 23 June – produced one of the happiest surprises of my life. It all started way back in March 1977 when I received a letter from my old friend Edward Halliday, the famous portrait painter who lives just down the road from us in Hamilton Terrace. He wrote that he had always wanted to paint me and would consider it a great honour if I would allow him to do so for his own enjoyment. I was naturally very surprised but thrilled. Ted is president of the Royal Society of Portrait Painters and numbers among his past sitters the Queen (goodness knows how many times), the Queen Mother, Prince Philip, Prince Charles and countless heads of state and VIPs from all walks of life. So I sat down immediately to write and say how honoured and delighted I was to join this galaxy of stars.

I imagined that he would show my portrait at the Royal Society of Portrait Painters' annual exhibition. I had to restrain myself from running as I went along to pop the letter through his letterbox. We had half a dozen sittings of about two hours a time and we thoroughly enjoyed ourselves gossiping and talking about every subject under the sun – refreshed every now and again by a glass of sherry. Ted and I had known each other from the old Television Newsreel days at Alexandra Palace. He had been the commentator and I used to go down there to do voice-overs on the cricket films. He likes cricket and knows everybody in all walks of life. So we were not short of conversation!

After the last sitting, Ted expressed himself satisfied, except for the background which he was going to make the Grandstand at Lord's with Father Time on the weathervane on top of it. At this point I hadn't even had one glance at the picture, though Ted asked Pauline to come along and give her opinion. I was putting off the shock for as long as possible.

With the cricket season in full swing I thought no more about it, presuming that Ted would tell me when it was finished. I had heard nothing by the middle of June when Barry and Clare told me that they were going to take me out to dinner on the night before my birthday. The rendezvous would be secret, but I was to be ready in a dinner jacket by 7.15 pm when they would pick me up.

This is what I did, and at the appointed time on the day they turned up to find Pauline and me all dressed up and waiting to go. They seemed rather excited about something but refused a drink when I offered them one, which surprised me as I had put a bottle of champagne in the fridge. Anyway, the reason for their odd behaviour was soon to be revealed. The doorbell began to ring, and in streamed twenty of my closest friends, all dolled up in evening dress. Bottles of champagne and glasses soon appeared from some secret hiding place and we all went into the garden and had a splendid party.

Then came another surprise. We were all summoned indoors and there was Ted Halliday with the completed picture – a present, I was told, from Pauline with the children providing the frame. Needless to say I was very touched but pleased beyond belief. The whole party and the picture had been such a wonderfully kept secret. It has all been Pauline's idea and she had organised everything, starting her planning in January, so as to make sure my friends could reserve the date. She had also contacted Tony Smith of *Down Your Way*, Peter Baxter of *Test Match Special*, and Paddy Davis, the marvellous lady who arranges all my speaking engagements. Pauline asked them all to make sure not to ask me to do any job on that day and sure enough it remained blank in my diary. It was certainly one of the best-kept secrets of my life and I had no inkling of what was up.

But there was still more to come. After we had consumed quite a bit of champagne, I was blindfolded, put in a car, and driven off to an unknown destination. I had no idea where we were going and didn't guess even when we stopped and I was led into a building, across a thickly carpeted entrance hall and down some stairs. Then I guessed it, as I heard the tinkling piano which could be no one else except Ian Stewart. So it was the Savoy, where all my friends had already arrived and we had two tables of twelve in the restaurant. We had a wonderful evening and danced into the early hours with a huge birthday cake with a cricket match being played on top, plus of course *Happy Birthday to You* from the band. What a lucky chap I am to have such a super wife and family, and so many nice friends, who actually paid for their own suppers! They had all been at similar sorts of parties when we were all aged fifty in 1962 and sixty in 1972. It seems that all our Mums and Dads must have had a rare old time in 1911 and 1912!

Oh, I had almost forgotten about the picture. I must admit that as many people hate the sound of their own voice when they hear it recorded, so do I dislike looking at pictures of myself. But Ted had certainly got a wonderful likeness, whether *I* liked what I saw or not. One of my 'friends' said charmingly that he could tell which was me as Father Time was holding a scythe.

One of the bonuses of becoming an OAP in London is the free bus pass to which one becomes entitled. I went to collect mine from the City Hall in Victoria Street, and returned by bus for my first free ride. It was quite an exciting moment as the bus conductor came along saying: 'Fares, please.' It was, however, slightly deflating that as I reached for my brand new pass, the conductor looked at me and murmured, 'That's all right guvnor, don't bother,' and continued along the bus without waiting to see my pass. Did I look *that* old?

Eleventh Over Dear Sir, I want to be a cricket commentator

I think this would be a good place in which to say a few words about cricket commentary. I get lots of letters from young boys who say that when they grow up they want to be cricket commentators (in my day it was engine drivers!). They usually ask how to set about it, how can they learn, and what qualifications ought they to have. It's very difficult to give a satisfactory answer, because so far as cricket is concerned, there is only ONE staff job on the BBC – that of BBC Cricket Correspondent. I was the first one appointed in 1963 and then after my retirement from the staff in 1972 I was succeeded by Christopher Martin-Jenkins. All the TV commentators are freelances and only Christopher and Don Mosey of the radio commentators are on the staff. The rest of us are freelances.

Any budding young commentator should read every book which he can get hold of about cricket. He should try to learn its history and absorb its atmosphere and do his best to understand all the laws and regulations. He should watch as much good cricket as possible and of course play it himself. If he can borrow a tape-recorder he should go to any match where he knows most of the players and practise talking about the game as far away from the other spectators as he can get. He should try to describe exactly what is going on and keep going for at least fifteen minutes without drying up. It won't be easy at first but he will find that as his confidence grows it will become easier to keep the flow going. The secret is practice and he mustn't mind if the other spectators think that he is mad chatting away to himself!

Another stepping stone to the commentary box is a job on the local paper or at the local radio station. The paper will help him put his thoughts into words and the radio will teach him the art of projecting himself into the microphone – ie broadcasting. The snag is, of course, that it's not easy to get jobs in either of these media but it is something well worth trying. In fact commentators on local radio do by far the longest stints of commentary these days except for the Test Match commentators. Another possible training ground is the hospital broadcasts which take place from so many county grounds. I'm never quite sure how the admirable people who give up so much of their spare time manage to learn to commentate in the first place. Perhaps they just practise on the poor patients right from the start!

And now for the art of cricket commentary itself. I don't think I can do better than repeat, in the rest of this chapter, what I wrote on the subject in the 1975 edition of *Armchair Cricket*, which I edited for the BBC.

It is an art for which there is no real school except experience at the microphone at the expense of the listener or the viewer. This is one reason why cricket commentators tend to be mostly in the thirty-five to sixty-five age bracket. It takes that long to learn! Nowadays, except for the ball-by-ball Test Match commentaries, there is little opportunity to practise commentary. Up to the mid-sixties there were regular broadcasts of twenty- to thirty-minute periods from county matches. Now it is usually only one- to three-minute reports, so that the budding commentator has no chance to test his ability to keep going for long periods, which is what the top commentators have to do. In addition a young voice lacks the authority of an older one and because of cricket's slower tempo this is more noticeable than with other games.

So, it's not easy to become a cricket commentator and more or less impossible without a large slice of luck, such as being available at the right place at the right time when the opportunity occurs.

Now for the qualifications:

1. Good health – 'the show must go on'.
2. A gift of the gab and the ability to keep talking.
3. A clear, strong voice which must sound confident. The accent doesn't matter, though in fact a dialect comes over

particularly well in cricket. But personality is important and can 'come through' in a voice.

4. The ability to put into words what he is seeing, which means that besides being observant he must have a varied and colourful vocabulary and a sound use of good English. The long periods of comparative inaction during a cricket match give the listeners an all too easy chance to notice imperfections in syntax or language.

5. And most important of all – for without it he can never become a cricket commentator – he must have a deep knowledge of the game, its laws and regulations, its customs, its record, its history and its players.

Acquaintance – or even better – friendship with the players is a tremendous asset and helps give an understanding of what goes on 'in the middle'. A commentator should have played the game himself, though not necessarily in the highest class. TV commentators these days are usually ex-Test cricketers whereas on the radio they are professional broadcasters supported by ex-Test players as summarisers. But then there is a great difference in the commentary techniques of TV and radio and there is no doubt in my mind that television is the more difficult.

Television Commentary

The first thing for a TV cricket commentator to realise is that he can never hope to please everybody *any* of the time. In fact he will be jolly lucky if he manages to please anybody *all* the time. Cricket, like golf, is a game played at a much slower tempo than most of the other televised sports such as football, racing, athletics, etc. There are, of course, many moments of excitement and tension but they are spread out over a whole day, and the action is anyway much slower. This means that the commentator's remarks drop like stones on a still pond. The viewer has time to listen and digest them and to weigh up their meaning and their accuracy. In the faster games a slight fluff or inaccuracy by the commentator is soon forgotten within a few seconds as a new situation develops on the screen. So the cricket commentator's comments must be concise and fit the picture exactly, and be well thought out and accurate while having to be made spontaneously at a moment's notice. This means that he must have a complete and expert knowledge of the game. He has to comment rather than give a running commentary, which is basically what happens with football or racing on TV.

So the cricket commentator always has to ask himself the vital question: 'When to talk and when not to talk?' It's easy to trot out trite instructions such as: 'Only talk when you can add to the picture', but it isn't as easy as that. First of all there is the expert viewer who plays or has played the game. He knows the laws and regulations, and all the players by sight. On switching on he only wants to hear who won the toss, the score, a report on the weather and an opinion about the pitch. After that he just wants to be kept up to date with the score and to make his own judgements on the playbacks after an appeal or a wicket has fallen.

I can understand this. A commentator on TV should, in my view, be like a knowledgeable friend who sits alongside you at a sporting event, and who fills in the details which you don't know. I enjoy watching cricket with a friend but if he starts to tell me what is happening, who so-and-so is or why the captain has moved a certain fieldsman, I feel like crowning him. I think I know and just don't want to be told.

But sitting alongside me there may well be someone who welcomes all this sort of information, and wants help with identity of the players and explanations of the laws. And so it is on TV. A large majority of the viewers are not cricket experts. I should know from some of the letters I have received in the past. What is a 'chinaman', 'silly mid-off', or a 'googly'? What is the LBW law and how many ways can a batsman be out off a no ball? Or once when I said that 'Ray Illingworth has two short legs, one of them square', a lady wrote and told me not to be so personal. Or when I said that Peter May was lucky to have made a century as 'he was dropped when two', back came a letter bemoaning the carelessness of mothers with their young children.

So, the TV cricket commentator has to try to strike the happy medium, knowing that there is really no such thing.

He will always have irate and dissatisfied viewers who will say either: 'Why on earth can't he stop talking?', or 'Why can't he tell us more?'

Radio Commentary

As he has no camera to help him the radio commentator must paint the picture himself – with words. He is the eyes of every listener and must describe in as much detail as possible everything he sees. As opportunity offers he should describe the features of the ground so that the listener who has never been there can conjure up his own idea of what it is like. It also helps if the commentator explains the exact position from which he is broadcasting in relation to the play. A brief description of the main features and characteristics of the players bring the game to life – 'he has red, curly hair, wears size 14 boots, scratches his nose before every ball . . .', etc. There is also more time on radio for details and records of players' careers.

All this information is useful to fill in the gaps which do occur during a game of cricket – when the fast bowlers are walking back to the start of their long runs, during the drinks interval or when the umpires go off to search for a new ball. But there is one cardinal rule: NEVER MISS A BALL. All this information must stop as soon as the bowler starts his run. The commentator must then describe in detail exactly what is happening until the ball becomes dead.

The art of good commentary is to get into an automatic rhythm with a description of:

The bowler running up.
His approach to the umpire and the wicket.
The delivery, the type of ball and where it has pitched.
The batsman's stroke.
Where the ball has gone.
Who is fielding or chasing it.
How many runs the batsmen are taking.
And finally when the ball has been returned to the wicket-keeper or bowler say how many runs have been added to the team's and batsman's score.

Only then is it permissible to leave the action and talk about something else, until the bowler returns to his mark. Then back to the rhythm again to describe the next ball.

Some Hints to Budding Commentators

1. Have light and shade in your voice so that during quiet periods you can talk normally and not too fast. Then when there is sudden action or excitement you can increase your tempo and raise your voice, though of course, without shouting.
2. Always think of yourself as speaking to ONE person, not to millions. You are that person's friend and guide. Tell him or her what you yourself would like to hear if you were not at that match.
3. Try not to talk over applause, especially when a batsman is returning to the pavilion after a big score. Let his reception register. This is often easier said than done, as there are many details about his innings to give to the listener before the new batsman comes out.
4. Try not to describe in too much detail how a batsman is out. Leave that to the expert summariser.
5. Remember that you are a commentator not a critic. So don't criticise an umpire's decision. Whatever you may think about it, he is in a better position to judge than you.
6. At the end of each over, give the bowler's analysis, the total and the scores of the two batsmen. Then shut up, so that the summariser can come straight in.

There is one problem which is common to both TV and radio commentators – when to give the score. The answer is as often and as unobtrusively as possible without interrupting the action, and at the very least whenever a run is scored and at the end of each over. This may be annoying to the lucky viewers or listeners who stay switched on for the whole period. But tens of thousands are switching on every minute and there's nothing more infuriating than having to wait for five or ten minutes before hearing the score. That's why in these days of an over taking up to five minutes it's a good idea to slip in the score during an over even if a run hasn't been added. In addition, of course, newcomers will want to hear details of what has happened before, so the scorecard should be shown on TV or read out on radio at least every ten minutes.

There remains one fundamental difference between the TV and radio commentators today. On TV with their galaxy of ex-Test players they nowadays concentrate solely on the cricket. They give an extremely expert and professional analysis of the play, with critical opinions on the captains' tactics and the skills of the batsmen and bowlers. But they are not encouraged to be humorous about the fringe aspects of cricket, which provide so much of the colour and fun – the fat member asleep in the pavilion, the bored blonde knitting in the crowd, the umpire's funny hat, etc. But, probably because they have more time to fill, radio commentators are given a freer rein, and indulge in more lighthearted descriptions and reminiscences, and a certain amount of friendly banter in the box.

But whatever the style of commentary one final word of warning to ALL commentators – NEVER MISS A BALL. If you do it's sure to be the one that takes a wicket.

Twelfth Over It's the Ashes! It's the Ashes!

After the glorious summer of 1976, England's victory in India, and all the euphoria of the Centenary Test, it was too much to hope that cricket could continue to be so lucky. Not only did the skies open for most of May, and much of the summer, but on 11 May the Packer affair burst upon the cricketing world. I'll deal with that later but meanwhile let's take a look at the cricket which was played in spite of the rain.

As soon at the Australian team was announced most of us thought that England had a good chance of regaining the Ashes. Except for the class of Chappell and the threat of Thomson provided he was fit, the team did not appear to be up to the standard of past Australian teams. It had too many players who lacked experience of playing under English conditions, and because of the terrible May weather, this weakness was never really overcome. Match after match played by the tourists was ruined by rain, so that by the time the first Prudential match took place at the beginning of June, the whole Australian team was woefully short of practice – especially the inexperienced newcomers.

On the other hand, English supporters had a new feeling of hope and optimism. The tide seemed to have turned and there now appeared to be a nucleus of promising young batsmen round the counties. There were also more spinners, possibly due to the high over rate demanded for county cricket of 19.50 overs per hour with fines to be paid by both county and players if the target was not reached. This meant that every county captain was forced to give his spinners more bowling than in the past. England, too, had a plentiful supply of the fast medium bowlers which are so much their speciality.

The only real lack was young, fast bowlers, though for the time being Willis was in great form. His career had been marred by injuries and finally in 1976 he only bowled 238 overs and had operations on both knees. But he made a miraculous recovery and took twenty wickets in the Test series in India, a fine performance on those slow, placid pitches. His success was largely due to a change in his bowling style. He straightened out his run-up, instead of running in on a curve. The change seemed to have prevented the various back and muscular injuries which he had suffered in the past. The other big factor in favour of England was the wonderful team spirit which Tony Greig had created by his inspiring and understanding leadership.

So, except for the weather all seemed set fair for a good season's cricket, and for the first time the three Prudential Trophy matches were to precede the five Tests, instead of coming immediately after the last Test at the Oval. This was an excellent innovation, as in the past there had been danger of anti-climax following so closely on the tensions and excitement of a five-day Test. These fifty-five over games also served as useful pipe-openers, and an introduction to big match atmosphere for newcomers to international cricket on both sides.

England won the series 2–1 but not without the usual alarums and excursions. In the first match at Old Trafford, Australia batted first and after being 2 for 2, finished with 169 for 9 off their fifty-five overs. Not a very formidable total but in the end England only managed to win by 2 wickets, due to two suicidal run-outs of Barlow and Greig.

At Edgbaston, England won by 101 runs which looks easy enough but their innings of 171 was not very impressive. Six batsmen made single figures, including three noughts by the Packer trio – Greig, Knott and Underwood. The Australian bowlers responsible were surprisingly Cosier – who had not taken a wicket on the tour except in the one-day match at Arundel – and Chappell. They both took five wickets, but poor Thomson trying out his injured shoulder for the first time in a big match was wayward and expensive conceding 46 runs in nine overs and being no-balled eleven times.

When Australia batted under heavy skies Willis (2 for 14)

and Lever (4 for 29) were too much for them. Chappell was
their top scorer with 19 and they were all out for 70 – the
lowest-ever total in the Trophy so far.

In the third and last match the Oval pitch provided more
runs. England made 242, of which Brearley (78) and Amiss
(108) put on 161 for the first wicket – a record for any wicket
in the seventeen Prudential matches since 1972. But again
the England batting looked brittle, Old (20) being the only
other player to reach double figures. Australia were going
well at 181 for 1, thanks to a superb innings by Chappell.
The match ended in farcical conditions, the game going on in
torrential rain, which even made it impossible to identify the
players from the commentary box. I have never seen cricket
of any class continue in such a deluge. But the next day was
Jubilee Day, and neither the teams nor the authorities
wanted to have to come back. In spite of the appalling light
and pelting rain Chappell continued to play magnificently
and his 125 not out was the highest individual score in any
Prudential match so far, and enabled Australia to win by 2
wickets.

There was to be no respite from the terrible weather when
the First Test Match was played at Lord's in mid-June. It
was one of the coldest Tests which I have ever attended and
in addition most of the second day was lost because of rain
and bad light. So the match was drawn with Australia still
needing 112 to win with only four wickets left at the finish.
This meant that England were perhaps unlucky not to win,
though they really didn't deserve to after their batting in
their first innings of 216. They were soon 13 for 2 and only a
stand of 98 between Woolmer (79) and Randall (53) saved
them from complete collapse. Underwood (11 not out) and
Willis (17) in a cheerful last-wicket stand were the only other
two batsmen to reach double figures. Thomson on his return
to Test cricket bowled fast and for him fairly accurately and
took four wickets. But Pascoe looked just as threatening and
nearly as fast.

Australia replied with 296, Serjeant (81) and Chappell
(66) being top scorers. In England's second innings poor
Amiss (0) failed again, being bowled by Thomson in each
innings. In spite of his new 'shuffling' technique he still did

not look happy against speed, but his partner Brearley (49) looked fairly solid. Woolmer (120) played another fine innings and supported by Greig (91) enabled England to reach 305 — but there were still seven batsmen who failed to reach double figures, including three ducks. Australia needed 226 to win but again Willis aided by Old bowled well and with the last twenty overs to go they were 71 for 5. Young David Hookes in his first Test in England came to the rescue with a fine 50, and so they saved the match.

The England selectors must have been pleased with the bowling and fielding but a bit apprehensive about the batting. The opening partnership of Amiss and Brearley failed twice and the middle order batsmen Barlow, Knott and Old were all out of form. But Woolmer looked real Test class with plenty of time to play the fast bowlers, and he began to look more and more like Cowdrey — but without his figure! Randall batted cheerfully and as usual looked as if he was enjoying himself. Unfortunately he developed bursitis on his left elbow and should never have been sent in to bat in the second innings. Greig, deposed as captain, received a mixed reception from the crowd but played one of his typical forcing innings which have so often saved England's bacon. His successor Brearley in his first Test as captain acquitted himself well in his quiet and studious manner. He gives a lot of thought to every move and acts with authority. He was the first to admit that his task was made easier by the team spirit already existing in the side he had taken over from Greig.

The Australians had not much to cheer them up in their batting, though their new boys Serjeant and Hookes did well in their differing styles. But the bowling, with Thomson's eight wickets in the match, and the aggressive speed of Pascoe backed by the steadiness of Walker, made it certain that the England batsmen would be fully tested throughout the series.

For the benefit of my Manchester friends who resent aspersions cast at their climate, I would like to record straight away that the Second Test at Old Trafford was played in gloriously hot sunny weather throughout. England's 9-wicket victory was their first success at home since 1974 and after it Brearley was made captain for the three

remaining Tests. Australia were bowled out for 297, their
top scorer being Doug Walters with 88, his top Test score in
England. The fact that he has never made a Test hundred
over here merely emphasises the different playing conditions
in England and Australia. In Australia a batsman with a
good eye can get away with playing across the line. Here the
first essential for success is to play straight.

It was a good all-round bowling performance by England,
all the six bowlers taking wickets. In reply England got off to
their usual bad start and with Amiss and Brearley both
failing, were 23 for 2. But then Woolmer (137) Randall (79)
and Greig (76) played splendid attacking cricket and
Woolmer with his second successive Test hundred con-
firmed his class. Likewise Randall once again proved what a
great entertainer he is. England's total reached 437, and
then it was Underwood's turn, taking 6 for 66 to help dismiss
Australia for 218. In this Chappell played a masterly innings
of 112 but except for Hookes (28) and O'Keefe (24 not out)
he could get no one to stay with him, six of the batsmen
failing to reach double figures.

Brearley and Amiss put on 75 for the first wicket, of which
Brearley made an impressive 44 before getting out with just 3
more runs needed. Then to the disgust of Bill Frindall,
Woolmer was sent in, which meant he lost the chance of
scoring three Test hundreds in successive innings. Amiss
was 28 not out at the end but still looked unhappy against
Thomson. With Boycott now lurking in the wings after
declaring himself once again available for Test selection, it
looked like curtains for Amiss, and that this would prove to
be his fiftieth and final Test.

And so it turned out – for the Third Test at Trent Bridge,
Boycott came into the side in place of Amiss, and with Old
once again injured, and Lever surprisingly dropped, Hendrick and Botham joined England's attack.

The Test was similar to the one at Old Trafford in two
ways – England again won – this time by 7 wickets, and the
weather was even more perfect over all five days. It was also
a sort of fairy tale with Boycott, the old boy, and Botham, the
new boy, getting the welcome touch from the fairy's wand.
Boycott's return was unbelievable. He batted on all five days

of the match and was on the field for all but 1¾ hours. Botham, besides playing a useful innings of 25, took five wickets in the first innings he bowled for England, and proved that he really can swing the ball in the air away from the batsmen under any conditions.

Australia, although again winning the toss, once more failed to reach 300, McCosker being top scorer with 51 and O'Keefe again left undefeated with 48 not out. It was a good performance by the England bowlers to get Australia out for 243 as the pitch was a typical Trent Bridge beauty. Although Botham caught the headlines with 5–74, Hendrick with 2 for 46 bowled quite beautifully and beat the batsmen time and time again.

The new opening partnership crawled slowly to 34 before Brearley was out, and then followed one of those collapses England supporters know all too well. Woolmer made 0 (so Bill Frindall needn't have worried), Greig 11, Miller 13. Then – horror of horrors – Randall in front of his packed home crowd was run out for 13 by Boycott who hid his head in his hands as the groans from the crowd made him realise what a crime he had perpetrated. Randall can do no wrong at Trent Bridge and it was a bitter disappointment to his thousands of supporters.

It was in fact Boycott's fault. It was his call as he placed the ball towards mid-on, but Randall could not leave his crease until he saw whether the ball would be fielded. As it was Thomson swooped on it, Boycott came on and Randall, starting too late, could not reach the wicket-keeper's end in time. Boycott was genuinely upset and the whole affair must have made him even more determined to make a hundred – something I'm sure he had in mind at the start of the innings. He was greatly helped by Knott who encouraged and comforted him, nursing him back to confidence, and together they put on 215 for the sixth wicket, equalling Hutton and Hartstaff's partnership at The Oval in 1938.

Boycott (107), although dropped at slip by McCosker when 20, showed all his old skill and technique in defence, and proved how much England had missed his powers of concentration during the last three years. But to me the real hero was Knott, who batted with all his best improvisation and brilliance. His 135 was the highest of his five Test hundreds, the highest by an England wicket-keeper, and he also became the first wicket-keeper to score 4,000 runs in Tests.

So, thanks to Boycott and Knott, England made 364 and led by 121 runs. In their second innings Australia did just pass 300 by 9 runs, with McCosker again top scorer with 107. This time Willis (5 for 88) bowled with great speed and fire and once again Hendrick's figures of 2 for 56 failed to match his great accuracy and movement off the pitch which worried all the batsmen.

The partnership of Brearley (81) and Boycott (80 not out) 'came good' in England's second innings and surely – but very slowly – they put on 154 and England won easily enough by 7 wickets. To the joy of the crowd their hero Randall made the winning hit in a bright little innings of 19 not out, some slight reward to them for their wonderful behaviour throughout the match. And of course also among them were many Yorkshire supporters who had come to watch *their* hero's return to Test cricket, and had witnessed a unique display of determination and dedication. Boycott had now made ninety-eight hundreds, and even then people were saying that the fairies were saving up his final triumph for his home crowd at Headingley in the Fourth Test. A hundredth hundred in a Test *by* a Yorkshireman, *before* Yorkshiremen *in* Yorkshire. Impossible surely, pure fantasy. But now read on.

In the one match which Boycott played for Yorkshire between the Third and Fourth Tests he made the ninety-ninth first-class century he needed to set the stage for Headingley. The odds against scoring three hundreds in successive first-class matches are extremely high. The odds against a batsman reaching his hundredth first-class century with the third of these are even higher. But the odds of achieving this feat in a Test match before your own home crowd must be astronomical. And yet I am sure that the majority of that large Yorkshire crowd on the first day at Headingley *expected* Boycott to do it. He himself, in spite of all his self-confidence, must have been one of the few who felt it was virtually asking the impossible. But in spite of losing

Brearley without a run scored, Boycott proceeded slowly towards his target.

Helped by some consistent England batting for a change, it took him over five hours on the first day. For the latter part of his innings the hundred began to look inevitable, and just a question of time. He finally reached it with a classic on drive off a full pitch from Greg Chappell. Even as the ball left his bat Boycott seemed to know that it would race down the hill towards the football stand for four. He raised both his arms above his head, waving his bat on high, and just had time to do a little war dance before he was swamped by invading spectators. Headingley erupted for several minutes. This was Boycott's moment and his alone. Remarkably the fact that if England were to win this Test they would win back the Ashes seemed to fade into the background. Remembering how much had happened in the few weeks since his return to Test cricket after an absence of three years, I rank this as one of the most unlikely and emotional feats I have ever witnessed on a cricket field.

Boycott continued to dominate the match on the second day. Would he make two hundred, would he carry his bat? Well in the end he did neither and was out after tea for 191 from England's total of 436. The luck was all against Australia. In overcast weather they found the movement and swing of Hendrick (4 for 41) and Botham (5 for 21) practically unplayable. Once again McCosker – brilliantly thrown out by Randall – was top scorer with 27, and besides him only Hookes and Robinson reached double figures. When they followed on 333 runs behind, the weather was still against them and Hendrick once again (4 for 54) and Willis (3 for 32) did most of the damage. Just before tea on the fourth day, Randall caught Marsh at mid-off off Hendrick and as he did so turned a super cartwheel to signify that England had won by an innings and 85 runs and so had regained the Ashes after two and a half years in Australia's possession.

This was a great day for Brearley and the England team and needless to say there was much revelry upstairs in the English dressing-room. Also being toasted was Alan Knott, who in his eighty-eighth Test had made his two hundred and fiftieth dismissal. But even as the celebrations went on inside, there outside on the balcony was Boycott savouring and acknowledging the cheers of his supporters – cheers, which in spite of the Ashes, seemed to be for him rather than for England. The prodigal son had returned in triumph. All was forgiven. In Yorkshire at least the 1977 Test at Headingley will always be remembered as Boycott's match.

Inevitably the final Test at the Oval was an anti-climax with the Ashes no longer at stake, and to make matters worse the wet weather *before* the match prevented any play on a perfectly fine first day. The selectors after much advice for and against, decided to play the three Packer defectors and the only change was the return of Lever for Botham who was injured with a bad foot.

Despite a good start of 86 by Boycott and Brearley, England succumbed to some fine outswing bowling by Malone, belatedly selected for his first Test of the tour. His figures (47–20–63–5) are worth printing in full as his was not only great bowling but a marathon effort as well. England were all out for 214 and in spite of some lively fast bowling by Willis (5 for 102) Australia reached their highest score of the series – 385. Their most promising young batsman, left-hander David Hookes, was top scorer with a bright 85, but the most notable stand of the innings was between Walker (78 not out) and Malone (46). They put on 100 for the ninth wicket. There was only time for England to make 57 for 2, including a nice little unbroken partnership of 41 between Boycott and Randall, one feature of which was their immaculate running between the wickets! And so the match was drawn and England had won the series 3–0.

Final Thoughts on the Series

England were undoubtedly the better team. Well led by Brearley they caught and fielded better than any England side I have ever seen. A fantastic one-handed slip catch by Greig at Old Trafford, another in the gully by Hendrick at Trent Bridge, and Randall's run out of McCosker at Headingley were typical highlights. The bowling strength was ideal for this country with Willis providing the real pace, and his twenty-seven wickets was a magnificent effort, underlying his fitness and the success of his new run-up. Hendrick, Old, Lever and Botham supplied the swing and movement, and they had of course the usual economical support from Underwood, who bowled more overs than anyone. There was also the promising but underbowled off-spinner Miller and that perpetual picker-up of much needed wickets Greig.

A special word of praise for young Botham who took five wickets in his first Test innings and followed it with another five at Headingley. He is an enthusiastic cricketer who could become a great Test all-rounder. He has a prodigious out-swing, is a fine forcing batsman and a good fielder anywhere, including the slips.

The batting I am afraid still gave me the willies but there were enough plus signs to be optimistic for the future. Boycott's fairy-tale return to Test cricket after an absence of three years was the outstanding feature. He provided a touch of class and a wonderful defensive technique. He is the *bête-noire* of bowlers as he allows them so little chance and he gave a much needed solidity to the batting line-up. Whether Brearley is the right partner for him is questionable, although on occasions their opening partnerships of 34, 154, 0, 86, 5 showed a certain amount of rapport. But both are slow scorers – Boycott by design and I feel he could and should accelerate – Brearley on the other hand, although showing plenty of guts against the fast bowlers, is probably just below the real class needed for an opening Test batsman.

Woolmer – now temporarily lost – tailed off towards the end of the series, but looked the part of an England No. 3. And what about Randall? I must confess that I have gone down on my knees on some nights and prayed that he would make enough runs to justify the selectors keeping him in the side. He is a breath of fresh air – the entertainer *par excellence*. Someone who enjoys his cricket and shows it. His fielding is an inspiration to the team and he regularly goes in to bat plus twenty runs or more which he has saved in the field. He is the only Test batsman I have ever seen who *runs* out of the pavilion to bat. Then with a hop, skip and a jump he hurries to the wicket, eager to get on with it. Note how many times he has about three boundaries in his first twenty runs. When he is standing at the crease I would recommend all young boys watching to forget what they see. He does nearly everything wrong. He fidgets, moves his head, shuffles his feet. He is never still, like the Jack-in-the-Box he is. But in the end he plays *straight*, his timing is sweet, and his strokes all round the wicket – including the much neglected cut – are a joy to watch. Test cricket needs more players like him. I am unashamedly his fan.

For some time at least England will have to do without the rescue acts of Greig and Knott, and the debt which England owes them will probably only be properly appreciated when they are not there. As I write Roope is the man in possession at No. 5. He is a good driver of the ball but somehow does not seem to me to quite fill the bill. But I hope that I am wrong if only because he is such a brilliant close catcher.

But there is, as I have said, much hope for the future – Gatting, Rose, Gower, Athey, Love, Tavaré, Cowdrey, Hopkins, Stovold – and so I could go on. England's primary need is for a couple of really fast young bowlers. They need not swing the ball nor move it. But they must have pace and the strength and physical fitness which is part and parcel of the great fast bowler. It is a sad fact that most of our fast men break down with alarming regularity these days – Willis, Arnold, Old and Hendrick are recent examples. One exception is Lever who just bowls and bowls without any apparent after-effects. But even Botham, aged twenty-one and strong as an ox, had to withdraw from the last Test with foot trouble. Why *are* there so many injuries and breakdowns in these days of expert physiotherapists, electrical massage and new exercise techniques? Alec Bedser has a simple answer. Young boys nowadays don't walk enough. He cites himself – 'and the brother' – who both used to walk several miles to school and back each day. This is the stuff to build the frame and muscles which a fast bowler must have.

I have another theory. This breaking down has become much more common during the last ten years or so. People like Trueman, Statham, Bailey and Bedser seldom missed Tests because of injuries caused by bowling. Could it be that nowadays too much time is spent 'on the table' and too little just bowling? Exercises and massage are all very well but bowling is a contortion in itself and calls into play some otherwise unused muscles. There's one other possible cause – the constant driving up and down the motorways, often long distances on Sundays in the middle of a three-day county match. How often does one see a team arriving in their cars after sitting in cramped conditions for an hour or two, and then going straight out on to the field without any loosening up beforehand. That must be a strain on the muscles.

But I have digressed as usual. We have some good spinners today, far more than a few years ago. Miller, Cope, Carrick, Pocock, Edmonds, Emburey, Graveney, East, Childs, Southern, Arrowsmith, Savage – the list is surprisingly large. And finally Kent have done it again and produced yet another wicket-keeper/batsman to follow Ames, Evans and Knott. Paul Downton – only aged twenty – is as good as any of them were at his age. I am particularly pleased that he was picked to go to Pakistan, as at the Oval Test I implored Alec Bedser to have the courage to send him. Luckily I was preaching to the converted, because by a lucky chance when Bedser went especially to watch Downton, he was standing up to the medium pace of Asif and got a brilliant stumping on the leg side. That would have especially impressed Bedser, who always liked his wicketkeepers to stand up.

As for the Australians, I cannot believe that the Packer affair did not affect their morale and concentration. Most of them had signed, but a few had not, and that must have caused some division. At any rate they never showed the fight and determination which Australian sides have always had. It was not their fault that except for Chappell they lacked class but all too often they seemed to play careless – I don't care – sort of strokes. Hookes was the most promising of the new batsmen, and I feel that both Serjeant and Hughes will develop as a result of the experience they have gained on the tour.

Thomson, though not so menacing without Lillee, took twenty-two wickets and was undoubtedly still very fast, growing more accurate as the tour progressed. Pascoe looked nearly as quick and was sometimes livelier, while poor Malone with his outswingers was badly overlooked by his selectors. My own feeling about Walker is that he is over-estimated, hard worker though he is. He is one of those bowlers, like Statham, of whom people say: 'He should have got more wickets. His analysis does not do him credit.' But unlike Statham, Walker does not always bowl *straight*.

Except for the Packer cloud it was a pleasant series from which both captains emerged with credit. Greg Chap-pell – in contrast to his volatile brother Ian – was always the soul of tact and remained cool and calm on all occasions. There was some good cricket to watch, and one of the features of the series was the size and good behaviour of the crowds. What a contrast to 1976! This time there was no running on to the field, calypsos or beer cans or ruderies shouted from the terraces. Any barracking was good natured. This was so at all the grounds but my prize goes to Trent Bridge where on five days of glorious sunshine record crowds just sat back and enjoyed the cricket and applauded good play by either side impartially.

Finally, of course, England won. That made a change and gave encouragement to the many hundreds of thousands of faithful lovers of cricket who either at the grounds, or through their TV, radio or papers, follow the fortunes of their country and enjoy nothing more than seeing Australia well and truly beaten.

In the county competitions, Middlesex were the best all-round side but were perhaps lucky to finish equal top with Kent in the Schweppes County Championship. Because Middlesex's Gillette semi-final with Somerset on 17–19 August was washed out by rain – and yet had to be decided in time for the final on 3 September – they were allowed to play it instead on 24, 25 or 26 August. In the end, because of more rain, they had to settle for a fifteen overs per side match on the twenty-sixth. This meant that their *county* match against Somerset scheduled to start on 24 August had to be played a week later. It so happened that on 24, 25 and 26 August the other two contenders for the championship – Kent and Gloucestershire – both had their matches abandoned without a ball being bowled and it is likely that Middlesex and Somerset would have suffered the same fate, as Lord's was never really fit for play – even for the fifteen-over Gillette game. As it was when Middlesex *did* play Somerset a week later they were able to pick up seven very useful bonus points.

But there was no doubt about their right to claim the Gillette Cup when they beat Glamorgan by 5 wickets in the final at Lord's. My chief memory of this match was a gigantic six hit by Glamorgan's young left-hander Mike Llewellyn. He drove a ball from Emburey right up to the top of the left-hand corner of the pavilion. The ball bounced on the roof of our commentary box and was retrieved from the gutter two days later. MCC say that had there not been a trellis in the way it would have cleared the pavilion completely. I must say it was quite frightening as we saw the ball coming straight for us as if it was going to come through our window. But luckily it seemed to get a second wind and soared over our heads. It was by far the biggest hit I had ever seen at Lord's, though in 1945 Keith Miller had hit one into our old commentary box over the England dressing-room. But that was a floor lower than our present box. Anyhow, I thought it prudent to wave a white handkerchief of surrender out of our window, in case Mike tried it again.

The John Player – as it usually does – provided another nail-biting finish, all depending on the last matches. As it was at the finish Leicestershire and Essex each had the same number of points – fifty-two. But as Leicestershire had won thirteen matches to Essex's twelve, Ray Illingworth's team were the winners. Ray's cunning leadership had finally got them past the post first, but I felt sorry for Essex who once again just failed to win their first-ever trophy of any kind, although for half the season they had been top of the table.

Finally, in the Benson and Hedges final, Gloucestershire beat Kent fairly easily by 64 runs – a great personal triumph for Mike Procter. His dynamic and sympathetic captaincy had inspired the whole Gloucestershire team to play some of its best cricket for many seasons.

Here is one example of what I mean by sympathetic captaincy. David Partridge did not bat in Gloucestershire's innings of 237 (in which incidentally Andy Stovold hit a brilliant 71 and the power of his strokes must have impressed the selectors). Then in the field Partridge dropped a not too easy catch in front of the grandstand. And so, although Gloucestershire were doing well and likely to win the match without his help as a bowler, Procter called him up to bowl and kept him on in spite of two expensive overs, until he finally got his wicket. Procter then promptly took him off. But by giving him his chance he had brought Partridge into the match and emphasised that Gloucestershire were a real team in which *every* man – not just the stars – played an important part. That's what I call captaincy.

Thirteenth Over In the box

The summer of 1977 was certainly a vintage one for our Radio 3 *Test Match Special*. Over the years the Press and listeners have been most kind and generous in their appreciation of our efforts. The idea, which we always try to get across – namely that cricket is fun and something to be enjoyed – seems to have caught on in a big way. In 1977 the fulsome praise which we received was really quite staggering, but none the less welcome for all that! There were big spread feature articles about us in the national dailies, Sundays and London and provincial evening papers. Some of the reporters and writers came and spent a whole day in the commentary box with us at one or two of the Tests to see exactly how it all works and what makes it tick.

The one thing which seemed to surprise them all was the friendly atmosphere, the lack of the alcoholic stimulants which cartoonists delight to show, and the apparent casualness of the whole operation. 'Just like a group of friends watching a match together and obviously enjoying themselves', said one of the writers to me. And I think he hit the nail on the head. To start with we *are* all friends and it's incredible but true that I have never had a row with anyone in the commentary box over thirty-two years. We all love cricket, enjoy watching it and talking about it – even living it. We are also all utterly different in voice, character and approach. By ringing the changes of the four commentators three times every hour the listeners are given a complete contrast.

The various boxes at the six Test grounds are basically the same in size and shape. Except at Old Trafford and Headingley they are all situated in the pavilion at balcony height directly behind the bowler's arm. Possibly because we have to make instant judgements we have always been far luckier than the Press in this respect. In only three of the Test grounds are they directly behind the stumps. At Old Trafford and Headingley the pavilions are sideways on to the pitch. So at Headingley we are high up at the back of the football stand, and at Old Trafford our box – the smallest and most cramped – is in the block which houses the main scoreboard and seats for the official guests. The boxes have glass windows which can be opened or not and ideally there is room for five people to sit comfortably in a row at a baize-covered shelf on which are four or five stand microphones. The summarisers – either Trevor Bailey or Freddie Trueman who change over every hour – sit in one corner usually with a small TV set in front of them so as to be able to study the action replays if they wish.

Next to them is the commentator, then a large space for the bearded wonder Bill Frindall, with all his books, score sheets, calculators and coloured pens and pencils, plus a thermos flask or two. On his other side will be another commentator who is 'resting' and then in the other corner a spare seat and microphone. This is used by casual visitors to the box whom we often interview – people like the manager of the touring side, Alec Bedser, chairman of the selectors, or the captains at the end of a match.

People often ask me about life in the box, its routine and what we do when not at the microphone or when it's raining. We all have our different ways of spending the day so I will only speak on my own behalf. I always try to get to the box at least an hour before play is due to start and can always rely on our producer being already there – either Peter Baxter in London, Don Mosey in the North, or Dick Maddock in the Midlands. They will have stuck a roster up on the wall and by the commentator's mike, showing our commentary times during the day – normally one twenty-minute period every hour. They will also have sorted out into piles the large number of letters which arrive for us each day. If I can, I always try to open mine and give them a cursory glance in case there is anything in them which I feel should be brought up during the day's play.

These letters are very welcome and reveal a faithful and seemingly ever-increasing band of *TMS* listeners. Some letters are just kind and say how much they enjoy the programmes. Some ask technical questions, others want information about records. Some disagree with something which we have said, or point out a mistake. But the great thing about them is that even when critical they are written in a friendly way without any of the abuse and rudeness so often posted to television commentators. Why this should be so I have never really discovered. But I do know that when I was doing television commentary I regularly received a small percentage of letters telling me to put a sock in it, or why couldn't I be like Peter West – or just simply telling me to get well and truly stuffed. Some of our radio listeners no doubt feel the same but they are either too polite to say so, or just don't bother to write. We each try to answer the more personal letters, some are answered from time to time during gaps in play, others get included in the listeners' letters session during the Monday lunch interval. The rest – as many as two thousand in 1977 – are acknowledged by Peter Baxter on behalf of the BBC.

One type of letter does create problems and that is the one asking us to get the autographs of the two teams and both commentary teams as well. Some even include autograph books or miniature bats. Others enclose treasured cuttings from old newspapers or photographs of past cricketers, which they want returned after we have seen them. If only they could see the piles of letters, small parcels and old envelopes littering the confined space of the boxes they would realise the folly of sending anything of any value which they want to be sure to get back. There is real danger of it being lost in the all inevitable chaos. As for the autographs – well, many years ago we had to make it a rule not to bother the teams. We get so many requests that we would become an intolerable nuisance were we to grant them, even if we could spare the time to keep on trailing off to the dressing-rooms. We do, however, do our best to send our own autographs though we appreciate that they are only a very poor second best. And by the way a stamped addressed envelope is the most certain way of being successful.

A word about the parcels. People are very kind and send us a varied assortment of presents. A lady from Bournemouth regularly sends us our favourite pastilles, another from Maida Vale personally delivers a bottle of wine at the London grounds. There's a lovely lady who keeps a flower shop in Hounslow who sends a beautiful bouquet at the end of each match. Other ladies send us cakes. One thing leads to another. After we had thanked someone for some sweets, the next day a dental centre sent us a toothbrush. When we thanked them for that someone followed with some toothpaste. A big sweet manufacturer sent boxes and boxes of their particular confectionery – so many that we could not possibly consume them all, and the local children's hospital benefited. On one occasion, for some reason, Greg Chappell lay on his back and kicked his legs in the air. I remarked that our Yorkshire Terrier Mini did this on our lawn as she had eczema on her back. Not only did this produce a shoal of letters, including two from Australia, but a chemical firm sent me some skin powder to put into her food. We really *are* spoilt and are most grateful to everyone for their thoughtfulness and kindness.

But I've digressed! Back to the day's routine. After looking at the letters and parcels I usually read the day's papers to see what they have to say about the game and to check in case they have got hold of a story which we have missed. Then I usually watch the players practising and get the latest news on any team injuries. After a cup of coffee it's back to the box for the start of our day's broadcasting – fifteen minutes before play on the first day and five minutes before on the other four. Once we are on the air the microphones in the box are 'live' so that those who are not commentating have to keep as quiet as possible. With about four or five extroverts this is not easy, and I'm afraid that the odd chuckle and whispered remark do sometimes come over the mike.

The lunchtime summary finishes at 1.35 pm and then we all go our separate ways. On some grounds we have a packed lunch or bring our own sandwiches. At Lord's I always picnic with my family on the lawn behind the Warner Stand. At Headingley I am lucky that Sidney Hainsworth, who sponsors the Fenner Trophy at Scarborough and also presented the Sutcliffe Gates to Headingley, gives me a slap-up lunch in the Taverners Tent. At Edgbaston the Warwickshire Committee generously entertains us, while at Trent Bridge we are royally looked after by the famous old Trent Bridge Inn. So we do pretty well but not, alas, on every day. As I've said on Mondays we spend the lunch session answering listeners' letters, and on some Saturdays one or two of us are needed for the phone-in programme *Call the Commentators*.

Most of the grounds provide us with a pot of tea and biscuits and these keep us going until close of play. Then after Tony Lewis has given his witty, expert and informative summary of the day's play I think that most of us feel that we deserve a drink!

During play when I am not commentating I usually sit watching at the back of the box. I'm still rather like a small boy. I dread missing a ball. But occasionally I do go out to stretch my legs and get some air, as I must admit that Fred's cigars and Trevor's cigarettes do sometimes clog up the box a bit! It's also quite a good thing to watch play for a short time from a different angle and I find that by sitting sideways on I can get a better idea of the speed of the bowlers and the pace of the pitch. The others, some of whom are writing for newspapers, leave the box more often than I do. In fact John Arlott likes to come in only a minute or two before he is due on the air, and usually leaves immediately after it.

When it rains we do our best *not* to return to the studio for music. We realise that people have switched on to us because they want cricket. They can get music on at least two other channels. So we talk about some current cricket problem or topic, answer letters, tell stories – though these are not all about cricket! As for instance at the Oval Freddie Trueman asked us out of the blue if we knew what was the fastest thing on two wheels. Naturally we didn't know. So he told us 'An Arab riding a bicycle through Golders Green'. Last season during one long stoppage for rain we kept talking for almost the whole session about one thing or another. The trouble is some people write in to say that they enjoy the chit-chat more than the commentary! So we had better be careful or we shall do ourselves out of a job!

Only when we run out of puff or material do we hand back to the studio. But then, funnily enough, unlike the players, we never play cards. We either just gossip or tell some of the stories which were not suitable to tell on the air. When Don Mosey is one of the commentators he and I play a word game on paper which produces some ding-dong struggles and keeps us out of mischief.

Finally a word of praise for our producers and engineers, who get none of the limelight and work for very long hours with scarcely any break. As a reward we make sure they get their fair share of the sweets and cakes. There are two producers for each Test. One sits in a studio back at Broadcasting House. He opens up the transmission and is responsible for filling in with music during intervals of play and giving the lunch-time and tea-time county cricket scores. He has to listen to every ball (poor chap) and can let us know if we are off mike, not giving the score enough or making too much noise in the background. He also has a large coloured TV set and there are occasions when he can help us out by saying up the line what is happening out of our sight – eg the Queen arriving, or something going on in the pavilion below us, which *we* cannot see, but which one of the TV cameras can pick up.

In the box itself is the producer in charge of the outside broadcast at the ground. He prepares the roster and sees that we keep to it! He arranges for people to come into the box to be interviewed. He cues us with a card when we have to greet *World Service* or *Sport on Two*. He tells the summarisers how long they have got and places a stopwatch in front of them. He arranges our tea and coffee, and, as I've said, sorts out all the mail and parcels. He encourages us, reproves us gently, but always keeps us happy. He is the most indispensable person in the box including Bill Frindall. Because at a pinch our producers can also score by the Frindall method. By the end of the day he must be exhausted, as he does not even get a break during the intervals, when he has to produce *Listeners' Letters*, *Call the Commentators*, etc.

I hope now that you have got some sort of picture of what

goes on behind the scenes in the box. It may all sound a bit chaotic – and so at times perhaps it is. But so long as you enjoy your radio visit to the Test Match as much as we enjoy being there, then we are all happy.

So that is how I see a typical day in the box. Others see it differently! We were much amused by an article in *The Times* in which Michael Leapman gave *his* impression of the way we carry on.

Now over to Brian Johnston at Lord's:

BRIAN Good morning. I'm afraid the news from here isn't too good. Play has been delayed because of picketing outside the Grace Gate by dozens of the less successful county players, who are complaining that they haven't been made offers by Kerry Packer's cricket circus. It's fairly nasty out there. None of the Test players has yet crossed the picket line except Mike Brearley, the English captain, whose fetching crash helmet is standing him in good stead at last. Now you know I don't like to get involved in politics, but this unfortunate incident does reinforce my view that the game isn't what it was. What would some of the all-time greats have made of a picket line, I wonder? I remember old 'Goofy' Grunwick, that great Essex wicket-keeper/batsman – the greatest player of underarm full tosses of his generation I should say, wouldn't you Fred? Anyway, I remember a policeman once tried to stop him getting into Lord's on the grounds that it was three in the morning and he was trying to climb in over the Tavern roof. He happened to have his stainless steel groin protector on at the time, so he just thrust his midriff into the policeman's face and knocked him flying. The policeman was fined for indecent assault. Pickets, I don't think he would have given much time to them. But here's Trevor and he's panting, as though he's hot from the fray. Good morning, Trevor, what's the latest?

TREVOR Good morning, Brian. Well it's looking pretty ugly out there. I was just on my way in when I happened to meet this old friend of mine that I hadn't seen since late last night and we decided to go to the Tavern for our first of the day. It was ugly, very ugly – that's the only word I can think of to describe it. It took us several minutes to fight our way through to the bar. 'Blacklegs!' they shouted at us, which was doubly unfortunate since my friend happened to be a West Indian. I think you know him – 'Fingers' St Paul, surely the fastest left-handed scoreboard operator of his generation. He and I were wondering what the old-timers would have made of all the fuss. Do you remember 'Goofy' Grunwick, the great Somerset leg-break bowler, who could make the ball turn on a sixpence, but lost his touch when they barred the use of coins on the field of play?

BRIAN   Yes, we were just talking about him. Let's ask Bill if he can look through his record books to see if there's ever been a picket at a cricket match before. (Pause and sound of record books being riffled through). Ah, here we are. He says no, there's never been one, but there was once a strike at a cricket ball manufacturer's in Peshawar, where the workers were campaigning for bigger stumps to be used. This would have shortened each innings, so you could have matches of four innings each instead of two, doubling the number of balls you needed.

TREVOR   Never came off, did it Brian?

BRIAN   It didn't, no. And now while we're waiting for the umpires to sort things out, I'd like to thank those listeners who've sent me little favours, as they always do. A listener in Glastonbury has sent me some wine gums packed in a pair of stout gumboots. She says I'm to suck the gums, wear the boots when rain stops play and fill them with champagne if England win. 'And if you're ever in Glastonbury', she writes . . . no, I don't think I'll read that, but it does sound a lot more fun than sitting here droning away about cricket. And another young woman from Bayswater has sent me a pair of undergarments to warm myself during the cold spell we've been having, though I must say they don't look too practical. She's sent me a limerick to go with them, which again I can't read to a family audience but I'll tell you the last line. It goes: 'Oh no, they're not mine, they're the vicars.' But let's get back to talking about the all-time greats. John has just struggled up here. What have you got to tell us, John?

JOHN   Well Brian you were talking just now about 'Goofy' Grunwick that great Worcester opening bat who still, I think, holds the record for scoring the fastest single in Test matches against New Zealand. I was just wondering if you remembered how his brilliant career was ruined in that famous Lord's Test against Pakistan. He went off to get another sweater and when he hadn't come back after an hour they went looking for him and found him *in flagrante* . . .

BRIAN   Really. I thought it was in the Long Room.

JOHN   Anyway, they caught him with the wife of one of the selectors and it was clear that he'd managed several times to get past her perhaps rather half-hearted defensive prods. Her husband did him a terrible injury with the groundsman's turf cutting implement.

BRIAN Never played again did he, John? He took up female impersonation, I remember. In fact I saw him in action a year or so afterwards in a drag pub near the Oval, doing an amazingly intricate exotic dance with a bat and a set of stumps. Fred, you come in now, who was the greatest performer you ever came in contact with?

FRED Funny you should ask me that, Brian, because I once came up against the wife of that selector myself. It was at a charity game down at Little Filandering on behalf of Prince Charles's fund for arthritic coachmen.

BRIAN Marvellously worthwhile cause, that.

FRED Yes, but unfortunately it rained most of the day and I was sent to help this lady make the teas and the upshot was that nobody got any tea and I remember coming away thinking that maybe Grunwick wasn't as goofy as people thought.

BRIAN That wasn't quite what I meant, Fred. Who had the biggest feet of anyone you can remember?

FRED Funny you should ask that because the wife of that selector I was mentioning had the most colossal pair you've ever seen. She played once in a women's Test and was the only player ever to have been warned by the umpires for wearing down the pitch when she was fielding at slip.

BRIAN Well, while we've been rabbiting on here, play has actually got under way and the Australians have lost a couple of quick wickets. But, John, you were going to tell us something?

JOHN Yes, Brian, it was about 'Goofy' Grunwick, the Surrey left-hander, who was certainly the finest extra cover of his generation . . .

Among the many hundreds of letters which we receive during a season, there is always a lot of poetry. I never knew there were so many budding poets and poetesses. This reminds me that a cricketing friend of mine once told me the difference between poetry and prose. He quoted the lines:

> *There was a young batsman called Walls*
> *Who was hit a terrible blow on the thigh*

My friend explained that these two lines are prose. 'But,' he added, 'had the blow been four inches higher, that would have been poetry'!

Anyway, after we had won the Ashes at Headingley, a

lady sent me this splendid parody on the famous Crispin's Day speech by Henry V before the Battle of Agincourt from Shakespeare's Henry V, *Act 4, Scene 3*. I was able to read it out at the end of the Fifth Test at the Oval, when we had some time to spare. I wish we had had Lord Olivier in the box with us so that he could have given it the rendering it deserved.

> *This day we won the Ashes*
> *He that lived this day and came safe home*
> *Will stand a tiptoe when this day is mentioned*
> *And rouse him at the word 'Ashes'.*
> *He that lived this day and sees old age*
> *Will yearly on the vigil feast his neighbours*
> *And say 'Tomorrow is Ashes day'.*
> *Old men forget, yet all shall be forgot*
> *Then will he open* Wisden *and show his record,*
> *And say 'These wickets I had on Ashes day'.*
> *But he'll remember with advantages*
> *What feats he did that day, then shall our names*
> *Familiar in his mouth as household words*
> *Brearley the Captain, Boycott and Willis*
> *Hendrick and Botham, Randall and Greig*
> *Be in their flowing cups freshly rememb'red*
> *This story shall the good man teach his son*
> *And Ashes day shall ne'er go by*
> *From this day to the ending of the world*
> *But we in it shall be remembered*
> *We few, we happy few, we Band of brothers*
> *For he today that won the Ashes with me*
> *Shall be my brother*
> *While others think themselves*
> *Accurs'd they were not there*
> *At Headingley on Ashes day.*

One of the most amusing packages contained two imaginary sleeves for a cricketing LP entitled *Bumper Hits for Six* or *When the Mighty Compton played*. Some of the suggested titles were:

> Hello *Dolly*
> Little *Dolly* Daydream
> The *Third Man* Theme
> John *Boles* and Gracie *Fields* Medley
> After the *Ball*

Ashes of Roses
Amazing *Grace*
I *Cover* the Waterfront
Run, Rabbit, *Run*
Bye, *Bye*, Blackbird
The Little White *Duck*
Oh, *Maiden*, my *Maiden*
Over and *Over* again
Kanhai Forget You?
Little Miss *Bouncer*
Close to you
May I?
High *Wide* and Handsome
Life is Just a *Bowl* of Cherries
Follow On
You're *Driving* me Crazy
Lords of the Air
Changing of the *Guard*
I Lift up My Finger and I say . . .
Varsity *Drag*

All these were sent in to us in two colourfully painted sleeves by Brian Orchard. We read them out on the air and this must have inspired a Mr D. B. Gardner who sent us these:

Try a little ton, *Denness*
Is *Younis* or is you ain't my baby
Thank *Evans* for little girls
Happy Days *Zaheer* again
Huttons and *Bowes*
Keep *Bright* on till the end of the road
Walters, Walters, take me to the altar
My funny *Valentine*

I was especially pleased to receive the above because it was nice to know that there is someone else who makes as bad puns as I do!

It might amuse you to see whether you can think up any more – the punnier the better!

And talking of puns there was one I actually missed and immediately received letters from two different people pointing out what I *should* have said. It all started with a man who wrote in to say that he was in trouble. He said his Afghan hound had chewed up the inside of his *Wisden*, and eaten all

the records! What should he do? I didn't really see what *I*
was expected to do about it but remember making one or two
rather wet suggestions such as that he should build higher
shelves or get a smaller dog. But as my two correspondents
so rightly pointed out the obvious reply I should have given
was that the Afghan hound should have his Wisden teeth
taken out!

Another piece of poetry was sent to me the previous summer by Mr Alan Hamilton of Torquay. He called it *The
Cricketer's 'If'* – (with apologies to Rudyard Kipling). I think
it sums up quite beautifully exactly what cricket is all about,
and explains just why it means so much to so many of us. Mr
Hamilton, who was eighty-five, sent a copy of the poem to his
old school, Wellington, where it was hung up on the notice-
board of the pavilion. Alas he died in 1977 but his widow has
kindly given me permission to use it.

THE CRICKETER'S 'IF'
(with apologies to the late Mr Rudyard Kipling)

*If you can keep your head when bowlers skittle
Both opening batsmen with the score at three –
When, knowing that your later batting's brittle,
You grimly think 'It all depends on me!'
If you can play defensive, watchful cricket,
Leaving alone out-swingers on the off,
(Knowing full well that, if you grope, you'll snick it)
However much frustrated watchers scoff!*

*If you can overcome unsure beginnings,
And start to push the score along a bit –
If you can play a really sterling innings
And play your natural game, which is to HIT
If you can score a hundred, and be master,
Yet shield your partner while he settles in –
If you can wrest a triumph from disaster,
And lead your side to a noteworthy win.*

*Or, if outwitted by a paceman's terror,
You see your middle stump shot out for 'duck'
If, still unruffled, you can note your error
And not just put it down to rotten luck!
If you can bowl a 'long hop' and get pasted
Yet keep direction and your length as well –*

If you can think 'That lesson won't be wasted –
I'll serve him up some teasers for a spell!'
If you can bear to hear, though sorely shaken
The umpire's 'No' to your assured appeal –
And realise you might have been mistaken
And show no outward sign of what you feel!

And if you can, when mid-off drops a sitter,
Curb your impatience and still play the game.
Reflecting that the poor chap's feeling bitter
And think 'Ah, well! I might have done the same'
And when, at length, you ache in every sinew
Your limbs feel leaden and your fingers sore.
If, when your Captain asks: 'Can you continue?'
You can still rise to just one over more.

If you can field with keen determination
Watching the stroke and ever on alert
Stopping the hard ones with anticipation
And never make complaint although it hurt.
If you, at slip, can hold an awkward flyer
Or run the batsman out from deep third man.
If in the deep, you catch a swirling skyer
And keep your head from swelling – if you can!

If you can mix with cricketers as brothers
And mingle with both teams at close of play –
And pass the spirit of the game to others
Wherever you may meet them day by day –
Although you hold no County Member's ticket,
And play your local matches just for fun:
You will have done a mighty lot for cricket
E'en though you never play for England, Son!

ALAN F. HAMILTON

Fourteenth Over Horse d'oeuvres

Towards the end of 1976 I had become slightly involved in a new sport for me – horse racing. I became part owner of a flat racehorse. And for those of you, who like me, know very little about racing let me hasten to explain that flat is not the shape of the horse, but records the fact that he runs *on* the flat and not over hurdles or fences.

I had done something fairly similar about ten years earlier when I owned one leg of a greyhound with Colin Cowdrey, John Woodcock and Michael Melford. As it was trained and ran in Kent and because of Colin's nickname, we called it Kentish Kipper. It used to run at Catford and won two or three races, though we were never there to see them. That's the trouble about owning a greyhound. It's not a very satisfying business. The owners have no say when it will run – that is arranged between the trainer and the stadium. They cannot see it *before* a race like you can a horse in the paddock, though they are very generously allowed to give it a gentle pat afterwards. We did once visit its training quarters but somewhat naturally the dog did not recognise us as his owners. We also went to watch it run once or twice, and it was amusing to see the way its price shortened when the bookies realised that we were there. They assumed we had come especially to back it – as if our measly £1 to win would make any difference to them. Another thing against greyhound racing is that the races are over so quickly you hardly have time to read the race, and even if your dog runs well, the pleasure is so fleeting.

So in the end we were quite pleased when Arthur Milton, the Gloucestershire cricketer and double England international at cricket and soccer, made an offer for Kentish

Kipper. Arthur said that he knew of a lonely little old lady down in Bristol who wanted a greyhound as a pet. He said he would give us what we had paid for him. So thinking that we were doing both ourselves and the lonely little old lady a good turn, we sold Kentish Kipper to Arthur for a hundred pounds. We thought no more about it for some time until a friend showed me a cutting from a Bristol newspaper, reporting the greyhound races down there. 'Kentish Kipper wins again!' was the headline. Arthur has always been a bit cagey about it and I still don't know how many races the dog won down in the West Country. But I strongly suspect that the lonely little old lady was none other than a stylish opening batsman, a brilliant close fielder and an England right-winger!

My entry into horse racing came about through David Brown the England and Warwickshire fast bowler. I suppose it started in 1967 during the MCC tour of West Indies. David met and fell in love with a very attractive girl called Tricia Norman. They met in Kingston at some sportsmen's gathering when Tricia was in Jamaica with her father, a well-known gynaecologist. She had always been a good point to point rider in England and while in the West Indies rode as a jockette in flat races against men jockeys. In fact we saw her come in second in a race at Georgetown, Guyana. It was a case of love at first sight and Big Dave – as he's called – had definitely bowled a maiden over. And to continue with cricket jargon, he soon got *hooked* on horses after they were married.

For some years, the Browns lived just outside Worcester where they raised a family and bred ponies. Dave had always wanted a farm and in the winters when not on tour used to study pigs and their breeding, so after a very successful benefit in 1973 they began looking round for a farm, which they eventually found near Kidderminster. They turned it into a stud and sort of livery stable, with masses of loose-boxes transformed from the old cowsheds. There they started to breed and break horses. They owned a mare called Santa Marta and sent her to a stallion called Grey Mirage. He was a class horse and among other races had won the Two Thousand Guineas trial at Kempton and had also broken the track record for two-year-olds over seven furlongs at Newbury.

The happy result was a strapping roan colt which Tricia brought up and broke and was the first person to get on his back. Dave asked me whether I would like a share in him and for a bit of fun I said I would. I brought in Martin Gilliat, and Dave already had the two Warwickshire cricketers Jack Bannister and Big Jim Stewart, and three others. We started as eight partners, but one fell by the wayside, so now we each own one-seventh of the horse – though which part has never been specified! And now for his name – and I'm afraid you are in for a bit of PUNishment. In order to keep the Grey of Grey Mirage and the cricketing connection I suggested that we might call him W. G. Greys, and surprisingly this was accepted by Wetherbys. He is trained by the well-known Midlands trainer Reg Hollinshead, who had his best season ever in 1977 with fifty winners.

W.G. ran in six races – he had a few weeks off with a damaged muscle and a cough – and he finished 'in the frame' twice. The other four times he ran well and never let us down, usually finishing about sixth or seventh out of big two-year-old fields with over twenty runners, after leading for most of the race. He is a big colt and stands 16.2 and the experts say that he won't be fully developed until he's a three-year-old, and we then hope his distance will be a mile. In 1977 he ran one 5-furlong, three 6-furlong and two 7-furlong races. At York in October we had our first thrill when he finished third in a 5-furlong race and then came our first taste of victory in November during the last week of the flat racing season. He won a 6-furlong race at Teesside Park by a neck but alas I was not able to see him win.

But Dave and Tricia were there to celebrate with Reg Hollinshead and his admirable stable jockey, Tony Ives, both of whom think highly of W.G. So do we all, and hope that by the time you read this, he will have proved as successful as the famous bearded Doctor after whom he has been nearly named. At this stage I am not quite sure what happens if he wins a really big race. Do we get a long leading rein so that all seven of us can lead him in? But after just one victory I mustn't get too cocky. Anyhow, it never pays to boast, as an American once found when visiting a small farm somewhere in England. The English farmer took him on a tour round the three hundred acres or so and when they returned to the farm after walking a couple of hours, the American said: 'You know, way back home in America it takes me two days in my car to go round my farm.' 'Yes,' replied the Englishman, 'I once had a car like that too!'

•During the winter when not doing *Down Your Way* or writing books like this, much of my time is taken up by speaking at lunches, dinners, or even at business conferences. Besides bringing in some useful lolly, it satisfies my urge to stand up in front of an audience and tell stories and jokes. This all stems from my admiration of the old stand-up comics whom I used to enjoy so much when I went to the music halls.

In the days before radio and TV a comic would tour the country using virtually the same act, year in year out. He might occasionally add to it, give it a bit of polish, or adjust it slightly to suit a particular audience. But basically it didn't change and I do much the same with my speeches. I have about three, which I normally use. One completely on cricket, one based on my overall BBC experiences over thirty-two years, and the third just an after-dinner speech, with jokes and stories – some true, some not. I have this absurd hankering to make people laugh, and get tremendous satisfaction from hearing the laughter after telling a tale.

There are virtually no new stories – just old ones in a different wrapping. It all depends on the way they are told and more or less everything depends on timing. I learnt a lot by studying the methods of the great stand-up comics like Max Miller, Ted Ray and Tommy Trinder. My wife Pauline often asks me how I can go on doing the same old speeches.

The answer is that each audience is different, and reacts differently to the same story. So that each performance is a new challenge. One thing I learnt from the comics was how important it is to win over your audience right from the word go. This is especially so with the Round Table dinners. The Tablers are a boisterous lot and very appreciative, but unless you do 'get' them at the start, they are inclined to barrack or interrupt. But another thing I learnt was to keep going at a good pace, so if one joke falls a bit flat, you are soon on to the next one, and hope for better luck!

I find the Tablers most stimulating and thoroughly enjoy my evenings with them. They are all under forty years of age, so are lively and quick to see a joke. They must be pretty near to what used to be a typical music hall audience. I treasure the memory of one of their chairmen who announced after the loyal toast: 'You may smoke now the Queen's drunk!'

I was told of one Round Table who thought up a most ingenious idea which amused me, though I know it shouldn't have done. During one of their more boisterous dinners it was reported to them that two Panda cars were waiting outside in the car park, obviously hoping to catch one or two of the diners with the breathaliser. So at the end of the evening their chairman found a teetotal Tabler (a rare bird!) and told him to go out into the car park and pretend to be roaring drunk, and then to get into his car and drive away. This the t.t. did, singing at the top of his voice, and swaying and lurching all over the place. He staggered into his car, and drove off very very slowly as if he was having difficulty in seeing. Sure enough the Pandas, thinking that they had a certain victim, followed him slowly out on to the road. They let him go about a mile, then one of them passed him, and signalled for him to stop. They asked him to blow into the bag and were amazed when it did not turn green. Nor could they smell any drink on his breath. However, since he had done nothing wrong, they just asked him for his name and address and then let him drive off. They realised that they had been 'had', and were not surprised on returning to the car partk, to find that, thanks to the decoy, it was empty.

I am also occasionally asked to propose the health of the bride and bridegroom at a wedding. Here I have quite a good tip for anyone asked to do the same thing. You inevitably have to start with a number of 'in' family jokes, but after that I recommend that you read out what the stars foretell for the young couple. You will find by just reading out what the astrologer has to say, that there are quite a few innocuous innuendos which should amuse the wedding guests – especially when they have had some champagne.

I recently had to do the honours at a wedding of the daughter of great friends of mine in Yorkshire. By scanning the London evening papers for a week or so I was able to read out one or two appropriate forecasts. Things like:

'You'll now be able to start on a job you've been too busy to deal with earlier in the week.'

'Probably the quietest day of the week — favours those of you who want to be left in seclusion to get on with what you want to do.'

'You'll be putting spare time this evening to practical purposes.'

And one especially for the bride:

'Be careful today if handling any electrical gadgets or tools.'

And for the bridegroom:

'There's nothing to be afraid of — it's just that you must be prepared to mark time and not burn up too much physical energy!'

In November 1977 I was asked to go back to my old private school, Temple Grove, to open a new gymnasium. The school used to be at Eastbourne when I was there in the twenties, but it moved to Uckfield during the thirties, and has been there ever since. There was a big audience of parents and boys, as after the opening the boys were going off for their half term. I remember the speech days which we used to have, when an Old Boy, who usually seemed to be a general or admiral, got up and waffled away for about twenty minutes. They normally boasted complacently that they had been no good at work or exams, and implied that it did not seem to have handicapped them in after life.

I hope I did not fall into the same trap. I kept my speech as short as possible and included a few jokes which were so old that they were fresh to this new generation of boys. The headmaster did a great job in introducing me to the parents, masters and boys, and never seemed stuck for a name. This was unlike a headmaster I once knew who was getting on in years, and becoming more and more absent-minded. At one speech day he was going round talking to the old boys, and said to one of them with a note of triumph in his voice: 'Ah, it's Smith major, isn't it?' 'Yes sir,' replied Smith. 'Well, tell me Smith,' said the headmaster, 'I can never remember. Was it you or your brother who was killed in the war?'!

Luckily I did not have to give away any prizes, or I might have had an embarrassing experience such as the actor Gerald Harper once had. He was presenting the prizes at the speech day of a girls' day-school and shook hands with all the winners as they came up to receive their books. Each time he murmured some innocuous remark like 'Well done', 'Congratulations', or 'I hope you'll enjoy this book'. After a while he got a bit fed up with this, and thought he would try something different, and more interesting. So when the next girl – an attractive blonde aged about fifteen – stepped up on to the dais, he shook her by the hand, gave her the book and said confidentially: 'And what are you going to do when you leave school?' 'Oh,' replied the girl somewhat taken aback, 'I *was* going straight back home to have tea with Mum.'!

Talking of embarrassment I like the story of the three middle-aged businessmen who were lunching together. They were discussing the most embarrassing moment in their lives. One said it was when he had forgotten to lock the bathroom door, and the *au pair* girl walked in, and saw him naked in the bath. The second said it was when his shorts fell down around his ankles as he was serving in a tennis tournament. The third man thought for a bit and then said: 'Well, I must admit my most embarrassing moment was when my mother caught me masturbating.' The other two were surprised. 'I cannot see why that should embarrass you. We all used to do it as boys. There was nothing to be ashamed of.' 'Yes, I know that,' said the third man, 'but unfortunately she caught me at it last night!'

This business of masturbation was of course always a problem at schools where they used to regard it as a terrible crime. At Eton quite a long time ago a boy was caught by his housemaster, who after giving him a lecture, sent him down to see the school doctor. In those days even doctors used to say it would make you go mad if you went on doing it. But this particular doctor tried a new tack. He asked the boy why he did it, and the boy honestly replied that he did it because he enjoyed it. 'Well,' said the doctor, 'I must warn you that if you continue you will go blind.' The boy thought for a moment. 'In that case,' he said, 'would it be all right if I went on doing it until I have to wear spectacles?'

Besides Jubilee Day I did quite a number of one-off broadcasts during 1977. There was my usual Boat Race commentary from Chiswick Bridge with interviews with the crews afterwards. Then came a telephone broadcast with Australia from the Oliver Messel room at the Dorchester Hotel in London. This was organised by Diana Fisher, one-time secretary in our Outside Broadcasts Department. Now she is one of the best-known voices and faces on Australian radio and television. She was over here on one of her hectic world tours, when, wherever she is, she has a hook-up each night with Australia and interviews stars of the entertainment and sporting world. On this occasion she wanted a couple of sportsmen so Ted Dexter and Denis Compton kindly obliged, with myself humbly representing the entertainment world.

We were royally entertained by Diana but received no fee, though come to think of it, Denis did make something out of the evening. When he got into the lift to come up to the suite he was joined by an Arab in flowing robes who somehow seemed lost. Denis is nothing if not friendly and was soon chatting up the Arab, and managed to direct him to the floor where his room was. The Arab was profoundly grateful and as they parted slipped a one pound note into Denis' hand. Better than nothing of course, and presumably free of tax. But on present Arab form it could so easily have been a thousand pounds or a diamond watch.

I took part twice in *Games People Play*, a light-hearted sporting quiz chaired by Peter West. There are two teams, each consisting of a sportsman and an entertainer, and my two partners were Rachel Heyhoe-Flint, who has an inexhaustible fund of sporting knowledge, and Pete Murray, Arsenal supporter and keen cricket and tennis player. I cannot remember whether we won – I rather think we did, but the result did not matter. It was just fun to do.

Mike Craig, an amusing Yorkshireman from Dewsbury, produces a programme *It's a Funny Business* in which he talks to people about the funny side of their careers. He kindly did me the honour of including me among such stars as Morecambe and Wise, the late Ted Ray, Arthur Askey, etc, and used quite a few of my old recordings from *In Town Tonight* days.

Then there was the *Archive Auction* in which Phyllis Robinson invited me to choose about half a dozen records or tapes for which I might bid if ever there was an archive auction. It was a sort of *Desert Island Discs* except that the choice was limited to material which had been recorded by the BBC since it started. Needless to say it is a fantastic and quite unique collection and one could have chosen enough records to make a hundred programmes. However I tried to make it as personal to my own tastes as possible and this was my selection:

1. *Tommy Handley, Jack Train (Colonel Chinstrap) and Diana Morrison (Miss Hotchkiss)* in an excerpt from *ITMA* recorded just after the end of the war. I chose it because Jack and Diana had been great friends of mine, and I have always considered Tommy Handley by far the greatest *radio* comedian, thanks to the brilliant way he could read a comedy script.

2. *A recording of the occasion in September 1938 when Neville Chamberlain left Heston Airport to go to meet Hitler in Munich.* At the time I was sharing rooms with William Douglas-Home and one evening his brother Lord Home rang up. He was then Lord Dunglass, parliamentary secretary to Mr Chamberlain, and had been told suddenly he too was to go to Munich. He wanted us to lend him a shirt as all his clothes were up in Scotland. He actually borrowed one of mine, so we thought we had better see them off.

I can still remember Mr Chamberlain with black homburg and umbrella standing by his (by modern standards) ridiculously small two-engined plane. He made the following little speech: 'When I was a boy I was always taught to be an optimist. When I return from seeing Herr Hitler I hope I shall be able to say – as Hotspur did in Shakespeare's *King Henry IV* – "Out of this nettle danger, we pluck this flower safety".' This

received a sympathetic cheer from the small crowd who
had gathered to see him.

On listening to the recording it is amusing to see how
broadcasting has improved. Before he makes his little
speech you can hear Mr Chamberlain say in a hoarse
whisper: 'Let me know when to start,' and then the
engineer's voice saying: 'O.K. Go ahead.' Imagine that
happening at London Airport today.

3. *Peter Bromley's commentary on the finish of the 1977 Grand
National when Red Rum created a record by winning for the third
time.* Red Rum has always been one of my heroes and I
think he is a fabulous horse. But I really wanted to pay
tribute to what is in my opinion the most difficult of all
forms of commentating. And I chose Peter Bromley
because I think he is the best of them all. A racing
commentator has to know and remember so many things,
and be able to produce these facts while giving the fastest
commentary of any sport, with the possible exception of
ice hockey.

Often at places like Newmarket there may be a field of
thirty comparatively unknown horses charging straight
towards him in a line, and often to make it even more
difficult, with the field split, half on one side of the course,
half on the other. The commentator has to know the
colours, owner, jockey, trainer of each horse and put the
right name of the horse to them, and at the same time read
the race and make sure to call the first three horses home
in the right order. How racing commentators do it I don't
know except that it does involve endless hours of
homework, juggling the colours and the names around
until you get them right. So far as I know Peter himself
has never called the wrong horse home, and what's more,
if a photo finish is asked for by the judges, Peter is always
prepared to stick his neck out and say who *he* thinks has
won. I take off my hat to the racing commentators.

4. Next came a nostalgic pre-war memory of *Harry Roy and
his Band from the Mayfair Hotel.* In the thirties after a visit to
the Palladium or Holborn Empire we often used to go
along to hear them, sitting at a table close to the band so

that we got to know them well. The piece I chose was 'Somebody Stole my Gal' with clarinet and a touch of singing from Harry himself, and plenty of that magnificent pair at two pianos – Ivor Moreton who did the twiddly bits in the treble, and Dave Kaye who provided the vital rhythm and accompaniment.

5. *The famous speech by Gerard Hoffnung which the BBC recorded at the Oxford Union after the war.* It describes his adventures with a bucket on a pulley at a building site, and with his high-pitched voice, gives me hysterics every time I hear it.

6. *Alan Gibson's commentary on the last over of the 1963 Test Match at Lord's between England and West Indies.* I had to have something to do with cricket and this was one of the most exciting Tests I have ever watched, not just because of the finish, but because throughout the five days fortunes had swung first one way, then the other. I was doing the TV commentary during the exciting last moments when with two balls left of the match to be bowled by Wes Hall, England needed 6 runs to win, with only one wicket to fall. David Allen was the batsman and he had just been joined by Colin Cowdrey whose broken left arm was in plaster. Had he had to bat he was going to stand as a left-hander and play with his sound right arm. But luckily David Allen resisted the temptation to hit a six for victory and kept out the last two balls safely. A draw was the fairest result to both teams.

7. *'Scorn not his simplicity' – sung by Adrian Hardy.* When *Down Your Way* visited Kilkeel in County Down during the summer of 1977 I interviewed a young teenage student artist who not only painted but also sang in a group. His name was Adrian Hardy and at the end of the interview instead of choosing a piece of music for us to play later, we recorded him there and then. The song he chose to sing was a haunting ballad composed by Phil Coulter, who among other things had composed 'Puppet on a String' for Sandie Shaw when she won the European Song Contest. Phil has a mentally-handicapped son and the title of the song explains exactly what it is about. I, for very

personal reasons, found it terribly moving, and just had to include it for my final choice.

My appearances on TV are practically nil these days, but for the last six years I have done the TV commentary on the Lord Mayor's Show. As in 1976 we were part of *Swop Shop* and before the procession started I was persuaded to offer a miniature cricket bat as a swop. The Lord Mayor was again wired up under his robes with a small transmitter and microphone so that he could give a message to viewers as the coach passed our cameras opposite St Pauls. When he had made his little speech the Lord Mayor – Air Commodore the Hon. Sir Peter Vanneck – thought he would make a professional handback to me, but unfortunately cued back to Raymond instead of Brian! Raymond Baxter had helped him at his Press conference about the show, and he must somehow have got Raymond's name stuck in his mind. But he immediately realised his mistake because our sound engineers heard him say as he sat back in his coach – 'Blast it! I should have said Brian.' Luckily, though, they had already switched back to my microphone, so his remark did not go out over the air.

The one other TV appearance I made was in Bruce Forsyth's *Generation Game*. This is a tremendous *tour de force* by Bruce and I can think of no one else who could anywhere near match his bubbling audience-winning personality. He makes wonderful use of the camera, and his various facial expressions after cracking a corny gag, which has either gone well or flopped, are real television. But no matter how great an artiste he is, much of his success is due to his professional preparation beforehand and all the hard work which goes with it.

It was fascinating to watch the rehearsal with Bruce putting stand-in contestants through the various games. He even read through the cards about each contestant and as he did so I kept thinking of what gags I would make about the various items on the cards. For instance one man had just been promoted to be superintendent of a cemetery. I thought my comment might have been – 'Well, you're *dead* lucky, aren't you?' As it turned out during the actual show Bruce remarked 'Oh, so you've got a lot of people under you!' His great skill is in making these gags appear to be spontaneous, though of course with the help of a scriptwriter, they have been worked out carefully beforehand.

After a daylong rehearsal Bruce has a two-hour break before the show. Then he goes out to warm up the audience just before the recording starts. The show is recorded on the Thursday evening before the Saturday it goes out, and ideally many of the audience are in parties and Bruce gains an immediate rapport with them. Incidentally, he does not meet the real contestants until they appear in the show, nor have they any idea of what the various games will be.

My small part was in No. 3 game called *Name the Commentator*. Five of us, John Snagge, Dan Maskell, Peter Alliss, John Motson and myself each in turn read out a bit of doggerel giving clues about the game on which we usually commentate. The contestants had then to write down who they thought each commentator was. One team guessed me, the other said 'Robertson of *Down Your Way*'; the male partner apologised afterwards and said his mind went blank. John Snagge and John Motson were each guessed by one team, but Peter Alliss and Dan Maskell stumped everyone. Remarkable really, when you consider how regularly they are on TV during the summer. One team in fact gave the hilarious answer of Virginia Wade when trying to guess Dan! Anyhow, it was all a lot of fun, and meeting the contestants afterwards cleared away any doubts I might have had about them being made to look fools. They had all thoroughly enjoyed themselves and would not have missed it for the world.

Oh, and by the way, the answer is definitely YES – Anthea *is* as gorgeous to meet as she is to see on the TV. If Bruce's stage musical activities prevent him doing any more *Generation Games*, millions of people of *all* ages throughout the country will greatly miss his delightful frolics.

Fifteenth Over Packer up your troubles!

And now, reluctantly, I must say something about the Packer affair. I have put off doing so for as long as possible because I personally feel it is all so very sad. Coming out of the blue as it did, it split cricket down the middle, put a severe strain on old friendships and introduced argument, resentment and rancour into the dressing-rooms.

Cricket was made the whipping boy and the cricketers the pawns (albeit well paid!) in what was essentially an Australian television battle. It all started because Mr Packer was refused exclusive TV rights for Test Matches in Australia by the Australian Cricket Board. Mr Packer – possibly out of pique, possibly to give himself a bargaining weapon – promptly set about signing up over fifty of the world's top players to play in a series of 'Super Tests' in direct opposition to the official Tests already arranged between Australia and India in Australia in 1977–8 and between Australia and England in 1978–9.

He did this in complete secrecy and I think what stuck in the gullets of old squares like myself was the underhand and deceitful way in which it was all carried out. That Tony Greig, captain of England, straight from the successful tour of India and the euphoria of the Centenary Test, could play a leading part in these signings, passed my comprehension.

Maybe because of the way it was done, the establishment overreacted. But if someone suddenly points a pistol at your head, your first instinct is to defend yourself and that is precisely what the ICC and TCCB set out to do.

All this has been particularly sad for me because nearly all the players concerned have been my friends for many years. Because of the clever way in which Mr Packer insisted on secrecy and silence as part of the contract, none of the first players to sign were allowed to consult their solicitors, their cricket employers or just friends like myself, before signing. Had they done so, there are so many things I would have wanted to put to them.

First and foremost, there is the question of job satisfaction. This to me is a vital column in the balance sheet of a job. All one read about in the law case were the moans from the players about too much travel, dysentery, separation from wives, the dole, etc, etc. *Why*, if they were so unhappy, did they go on playing? It was of course a very false picture. I have been on ten tours and have shared the players' enjoyment and thrills in playing cricket round the world, seeing new places and meeting friendly and hospitable people. I *know* they have enjoyed themselves and have considered themselves lucky compared with the nine to five commuter, the miner, the bus driver and so on.

Of course, hotels are sometimes tatty, aeroplanes break down, some food is lousy and one misses one's family. But this happens to thousands of businessmen, merchant seamen and members of the Forces as well as cricketers. In general the hotel and travel arrangements on tours are absolutely first class.

Much was made by their counsel of the fact that some cricketers have had to go on the dole during the winter. What did not come out in the papers was that the player who complained in the courts that he, an England cricketer who had had to go on the dole, was in fact writing a book at the time for which he had received a fat advance! But of course most cricketers do find winter employment, many of them going to coach in sunny climes, and others having part-time jobs with firms in this country. Ironically, in the old days cricketers were paid a salary spread over the year. But this was changed to an April to September engagement, so that they *could* qualify for the winter dole if they wanted it.

Anyhow, my point is that a cricketer's lot is a happy one compared with so many other professions and jobs, and that this *must* count when weighing up its value. I would also have tried to remind my friends of that seemingly old-fashioned word loyalty – to those who discovered them, coached them and developed their skills and techniques by advice or playing alongside them. They also owe a very special loyalty to their faithful supporters who either subscribed to or worked so hard to organise the many fund-raising schemes for their tax-free benefits.

And now for perhaps the most important thing of all. What about pride in playing for one's country or county and trying to win the Ashes or the County Championship? Surely this must be worth *something* even in these commercial days? Did they really stop to think what it would be like to play on vast rough football grounds on a dummy pitch in a concrete tray before huge empty stands? Did they really want floodlights, white balls, black sightscreens, microphones dug into the grass around the stumps, or someone asking them what they thought of the umpire's decision as they returned to the pavilion? I doubt it, if they were honest. But nevertheless whenever they were asked to comment on their signing, time and time again out came the phrase: 'It's an offer I couldn't refuse.'

So let's look at the money side, and here the players are on a better wicket. I don't think there is anyone who would deny that the average county cricketer has for years been underpaid, even taking into account the pleasing nature of his job. This is especially evident when comparisons are made with the average soccer player. A county cricketer who does not play for England earns anything between three to four thousand pounds for five months, depending on his county and his share of the various competition money prizes. In other words, a player from a top county will probably earn not only a higher basic salary but be more likely to pick up bigger perks by appearing in more semi-finals and finals. On average the successful soccer player in the first division earns about ten thousand pounds a year and again the player in a successful club gets more in bonuses and win money.

But there are several things to remember. A soccer season is for eleven months, not five, and it is a more physical game (loud boos from anyone who has had to face Lillee and Thomson!). So the playing life of a soccer player is generally much shorter than a cricketer, nor does he get one – or even two – *tax-free* benefits 'worth nowadays anything from twenty-five to fifty thousand pounds. Which of us can save that sort of money these days? But just a word about these benefits. They are tax free because of a case won by J. Seymour of Kent in the 1920s. This case established that benefits are not guaranteed nor part of a cricketer's contract. They are just gifts given by a grateful county and its supporters after no specific time, though it is usual for them to be granted to a player after he has been capped for ten years. The soccer benefits, however, are part of the player's contract and so become taxable.

Cricket benefits and testimonials have been granted since well before the end of the last century. But I do agree with the modern cricketers who find them degrading. Public appeals, collections and getting your friends and supporters to help, must be embarrassing. I know I should loathe it. The final reward undoubtedly makes it worthwhile in the end. But in principle cricketers should be paid sufficient for the job they do, and not have to rely on charity.

Cricketers who represent their countries have of course done much better. Test Match fees (in 1977 two hundred and ten pounds per Test plus a win bonus of two hundred and fifty pounds) have been laughably low compared with money earned by top players in other sports. Things, though, are now much brighter with one thousand pounds for each Test and five thousand pounds for an overseas tour. But the regular Test cricketers – say about fifteen in England – do get considerable spin-offs like writing books or articles, TV and radio interviews and quizzes, sponsorship of cricket equipment, private tours, and top coaching jobs. Many firms too give them quite lucrative jobs in order to cash in on their names. I would be surprised if over twelve months these top England players have not been earning either side of five figures with one or two considerably more. Not great money people may say compared to sportsmen like tennis players, golfers, boxers, racing drivers and speedway riders.

True enough, but these are in the main individual sports and the really big money is associated with a sport that takes place in America where the huge prizes are. That is where our own tennis players and golfers go in order to get into the big time. But even so it is still only the *top* players who earn the gigantic sums we read about. Ask the professional golfer how he does if he fails to finish in the prize money. He has to find his own travel and subsistence expenses himself.

If only America would take up cricket! But the truth is that cricket in England has always had to be subsidised. In the old days there were rich private patrons, then came the pools and now sponsorships, even including the County Championship and Test Matches. Cricket has for too long been run by badly paid secretaries – many of them retired officers. Each club also has many hard working volunteers who devote all their free time to cricket. So there are no bureaucratic administrators in cricket who are paid money which otherwise would go to the players.

I would certainly agree that cricket should have become more businesslike and more understanding of the economic difficulties of the players. For instance, I think that membership subscriptions are absurdly low for counties with Test Match grounds where their members can see the Tests for nothing. The Packer affair would probably never have happened if the players had been given more businesslike contracts offering more long-term security.

It's no secret, I believe, that up to 1977 Alan Knott had no contract with Kent whatsoever. It was done on a basis of saying in September – 'Goodbye – see you next April.' So perhaps you cannot really blame the players for snatching at a lifeline which offered untold gold and some short-term security. 'It's an offer I couldn't refuse. I've got my wife and children to consider.' They have all said it and meant it – and yet.

If the Packer 'Super' Tests succeed what will be the effect on our cricket? So far the signings have undoubtedly nudged the authorities to hasten the Cornhill Insurance Sponsorship for Tests (it was already being discussed before Mr Packer came along) and the counties to try and be more professional and realistic with their contracts. But if the Super Tests succeed then official Tests are bound to suffer. There cannot be two Test series competing side by side for public support. If the official Tests lose, then the rich Packer players will get richer and the ordinary first-class cricketer will get poorer – because the living of the average county cricketer comes from Test Match profits. It is as simple as that. That is why the players themselves voted FOR the ban against Packer players at the Cricketers' Association meeting.

So where do we go from here? I am sure that eventually there must be a compromise. There has to be, or top cricket as we know it will slowly strangle itself to death. Who will hold the cards at the end of the winter season is anyone's guess. But I would think that when each side has taken stock there will be some sort of suggestion to hold the Packer series in October and November and so leave his players free to play for their countries on winter tours. In return I suppose that the Packer matches might be given first-class status and allowed to be played on Test grounds, so long as they keep to the laws of cricket.

But there are two snags here. Will Mr Packer abandon his demand for exclusive Test coverage and how will the players react to playing eleven months of the year? For a long time now they have been complaining of too much cricket and calling for shorter tours – rightly in my opinion. If this compromise came about they would only have a few weeks off in September and March. But of course money does help! Though pity the poor fast bowlers. How *will* their feet stand up to it?

As I write it is too early to judge who is winning. Mr Packer's five-day 'Tests' have got off to a bad start so far as attendances at the grounds are concerned. He has, so we are told, even had to use dubbed applause to cover up the embarrassingly small crowds. As I had suspected – and hoped – matches between the world's top cricket players, however good they are, will not draw spectators if it does not matter to *them* who wins. They can admire the superb techniques, the magnificent stroke play and the fastest bowling in the world. But this soon begins to pall unless there is the necessary tension. The players on the other hand *are* trying hard enough, since there is an extra thousand pounds or so for each member of the winning team which CANNOT be shared with the losers, as it is recorded for income tax.

Due to the holiday period in Australia most of the TV ratings have been inconclusive, though on the evidence seen they must have been a disappointment to Packer, as has also been the support of the vital advertisers.

But he must certainly be encouraged by two things. The TV camera coverage has by all accounts been superb – eight cameras giving pictures and re-plays in various degrees of slow motion and magnification from all parts of the ground. And undoubtedly limited-over cricket under floodlight has caught on and provided thrilling finishes in front of crowds of twenty thousand.

So I suspect that this will be the Packer future – night cricket with the stars on the field as well as in the sky. He *may* try to compete with the Australia–England series in 1978–9 but I doubt whether it will succeed if he does. I suspect that unless spectators can become involved over five days, his 'Tests' will slowly die the death.

And now a final word about the ICC and TCCB ban on the Packer players from playing for their countries and counties. In the thirty-one-day court case brought by Mr Packer, Mr Justice Slade declared this ban illegal and to be an incitement to the players to break their contracts with Mr Packer. Ironically, if the cricket authorities had done absolutely nothing until next summer and then just not have picked the players all would apparently have been legal. If the judgement was based on such a simple point of law it makes me wonder why the trial was allowed to meander along for thirty-one days, with witness after witness just giving his opinion of the whole affair. I may be wrong but I would say that the only opinion that matters is that of the Judge. Could it not have been given sooner and so have saved the huge costs of two hundred and fifty thousand pounds which the cricket authorities now have to pay.

So what *will* happen about the ban? I must say that without being vindictive I was always in favour of it – I just could not see how the players could serve two masters – especially when their Packer series next winter would clash with the Australia v. England Tests. I think that the countries and counties will now go their own way. Australia did not choose *their* players for their West Indies tour – the West Indies did choose theirs, and now Pakistan – after some dithering – have left their Packer players out of their team touring England.

My bet is that England will not choose her Packer players again for England. I may well be wrong but there is no way that the law can force the selectors to choose them. The selectors will want to build up the side that has toured during the winter and prepare it for the Australia series in 1978–9. I myself believe this is only fair to the players who went to Pakistan and New Zealand, and that they would not welcome the return of the Packermen. The counties are in a different position. Those with Packer players who have contracts will have to honour those contracts – not necessarily by *playing* the players but by *paying* them.

Gloucestershire, I am sure, will be delighted to welcome back Procter, who achieved so much for them in 1977. What Kent will do is more problematical.

As I said at the start it is all very sad, and poor old cricket faces some difficult days ahead. But no matter if TV ratings do give victory to Mr Packer, I'm sure that cricket will get over it, and that in the years ahead we shall see a number of bright new stars playing for England. It's a great opportunity for them – thanks to Mr Packer.

Sixteenth Over I can't help laughing

(If you don't like corny jokes – skip this chapter!)

A man had just returned from his honeymoon and was asked by a friend whether he had enjoyed it.

'Yes, I certainly did,' he replied. 'I never knew you could have so much fun without laughing.'

I can see what he meant and of course it *is* possible to have fun without making a noise to prove it. But most of us, when hearing, seeing or experiencing something funny, do usually show our approval or enjoyment by a guffaw, chuckle, chortle, giggle, snigger or at least a gentle titter. I have been lucky in that throughout my life I have spent a lot of time laughing. So much so that I have often been accused of not taking anything seriously. Not true really, but I know what people mean. I have been blessed(?) with a sense of the ridiculous and a vivid imagination, plus a mind which is automatically tuned to trying to make a pun or joke at every possible opportunity.

There are so many different types of humour and I'm afraid that most of the things which make us laugh are usually jokes against or about other people. There are the usual things that happen to them such as slipping on a banana skin or falling accidentally fully-clothed into a swimming pool. There are the physical characteristics like a funny walk, a stutter or a comic face. I suppose one of the biggest laughter-makers is the pricking of pomposity or the humbling of authority. Try not to laugh if someone like a bishop or a schoolmaster sits on a well-placed whoopee bag! Hardest of all, of course, is the ability to laugh at yourself when things happen to *you* – then somehow it doesn't seem quite so amusing!

There is perhaps an even greater variety of *verbal* humour. Wit, satire and sarcasm come lowest on my list. Farce, slapstick, jokes, cross-talk, shaggy dog stories and quick-fire gags make me laugh the most. At the end of my last book *It's Been a Lot of Fun* I included six stories which always make me laugh. This time I will mix some jokes with the stories and place them all under various headings. Once again I hope some of them will tickle your particular sense of humour and anyway they could always come in useful for that speech you are due to make at your niece's wedding or at the village cricket or football club dinner. There are also – I hope – one or two which would be suitable for an old girls' gathering!

Animal

A man was telling a friend about the two elephants which were walking up Bond Street. One of the elephants told the other that he wanted to fart. 'Oh,' said the other elephant, 'you can't do that here. It will make far too much noise in a narrow street like this. You will have to go and do it in Hyde Park.' So the two elephants set off up Piccadilly towards Hyde Park. The man then asked his friend: 'Have you heard it?' to which his friend replied: 'No.' 'Well,' said the man, 'you would have done if you had been in Hyde Park.'

A lady had a pet dog which was one of those tiny chihuahuas. Its hair began to fall out so she went to her local chemist and asked him if he had anything to stop hair falling out. He went to a shelf and produced a pot of ointment. 'Rub this in twice daily, but there must be no friction, so don't wear a hat for a week.' 'Oh,' said the lady, 'it's not for my head, it's for my chihuahua.' 'In that case,' said the chemist, 'I would advise you not to ride a bike for a fortnight!'

Two flies were sitting on Robinson Crusoe. One of them flew off and called out to the other, 'Bye Bye. See you on Friday!'

Courts

JUDGE (to the accused who had just been found guilty by the Jury): Before I sentence you, what would you like to say?
ACCUSED: F—— all, m'lord.
JUDGE (to his clerk): What did he say?
CLERK (in a whisper): F—— all, m'lord.
JUDGE (to clerk): Oh, no. He definitely said something. I saw his lips move.

It was a hot summer's day in court and getting on for lunchtime. In the witness-box was a girl who had been raped and she was being cross-examined by counsel.
COUNSEL: . . . And what happened then?
GIRL WITNESS: He drove into a field, stopped the car and put his hand inside my dress.
JUDGE (looking at his watch): And there I think we will leave it until after lunch.

Three magistrates were trying a case of suspected rape. One of them was a retired colonel who had fallen asleep after a good lunch. Another was the local grocer, and the chairman was a somewhat prim ex-headmistress. The bashful young girl in the box was giving details of what had happened. The lady chairman asked her how it all started and what the man had said to her. The girl blushed. 'I'd rather not say it in public,' she pleaded. 'Very well,' said the chairman, 'write it down then on a piece of paper.'

This the girl did and the piece of paper was handed up to the bench. The chairman read it and then handed it to the grocer who glanced at it and nodded. The chairman then turned to the colonel who was still asleep, snoring fitfully. She nudged him and whispered into his ear, 'Wake up colonel, I've got something for you to read,' and thrust the note under his nose.

He woke with a start, saw the piece of paper and quickly put on his specs and read: 'I am feeling randy. What about a poke?' The colonel looked at the lady chairman for a second or two in amazement and disbelief. 'Madam,' he said in a hoarse whisper, 'you must have gone out of your mind!'

Doctors

A man went to see a doctor in a terrible panic.

'Doctor,' he said, 'please examine me at once. I think I'm going to have a baby.'

The doctor examined him and said, 'By God, you're right. This will cause a great sensation when I tell my colleagues in Harley Street.'

'So it will back home in Laburnam Crescent,' said the man. 'I'm not even married.'

A man went to the doctor with a very bad cough. The doctor gave him a large dose of cascara. The man was very surprised. 'Cascara doesn't cure a cough,' he said. 'No, I know it doesn't,' said the doctor. 'But it will stop you coughing. After a dose like that you won't dare to.'

A doctor was telling a friend about a nun who had terrible hiccoughs which she couldn't stop. So in desperation she went to the doctor, who, after a short examination, told her she was pregnant. 'Goodness me,' said his friend, 'was she really?' 'No,' said the doctor, 'of course not. But it cured her hiccoughs!'

A woman went to her doctor with a bad cough. After examining her throat he asked her, 'Do you ever get a tickle in the morning?' 'Well, I used to, Doctor,' she replied, 'but not now. We've changed the milkman.'

A man had that very painful 'universal complaint'. The doctor examined his backside and said he would like to try out a new cure he had just heard about. The man agreed and the doctor inserted a lot of tea leaves in the appropriate place, saying it would take two or three weeks to effect the cure. But after a week the pain was still there so the man became impatient and decided to go to a more orthodox doctor in the next town. He told him what was wrong and after the examination the doctor said: 'Well, I'm afraid there's nothing I can do for you except to give you some ointment. But I'll tell you one thing. You are going on a long journey with a strange lady!'

Food and wine

A man attended a club dinner and was disgusted at the quality of the food. So he wrote to the secretary to complain about it, and received the following reply: 'Thank you for your letter and I am so sorry that you did not enjoy the food at our dinner the other night. Will you please bring it up at the annual general meeting?'

A guest sitting at the top table at a dinner got only one glass of wine to drink the whole evening. But he got his own back on his hosts. It was his task to propose the toast of 'Absent Friends' – and he coupled it with the name of the wine waiter!

Football

A team of elephants was playing a team of mice. One of the elephants trod on a mouse and killed it. The referee took the elephant's name and gave a penalty. The elephant was very apologetic. 'I'm sorry, ref,' he said. 'I didn't mean to do it. I was only trying to trip him up.'

A team of insects were playing and for most of the first half they were a man short. The missing player was a centipede who ran on to the field thirty-five minutes late. 'I'm sorry,' he said to his captain, 'it took me longer than I thought it would to do up all my boots.'

A little boy was lost in the vast crowd at a football match. A policeman saw him crying so went up to him and asked him what was wrong. 'I've lost my Dad.' The policeman looked about him and asked, 'What's he like, son?' 'Beer and women,' replied the small boy.

A league side was doing very badly and languishing at the bottom of the table. Needless to say their gates were very poor and attendances had dwindled to a few hundreds. A man rang up the manager one Friday and asked: 'What time does the match start tomorrow?' Back came the immediate reply: 'What time can you get here?'

Another side had such poor crowds that before each match the public address announcer used to announce the names of the crowd to the two teams!

Good news – Bad news

An officer out with a patrol in the desert called his men together at an oasis one night. 'Men,' he said, 'we have been out in the desert for six weeks, we are miles from anywhere and quite frankly we are lost. But I have two bits of news for you, one bad, one good. I'll give you the bad first. We have run out of rations and from now on we will have to live on camel dung.' There was a groan of disgust from the men. 'But, wait for it,' the officer said, 'here's the good news. There's plenty of it.'

The slave driver on a ship went down into the hold to address the slaves who were all sitting manacled together rowing as hard as they could. 'Slaves,' he said, 'I've got some good news for you. You may have half an hour's rest.' The slaves sank exhausted at their oars. 'But, listen,' said the slave driver, 'here's the bad news. When you have had your rest the Captain wants to go water-skiing.'

Honeymoons

The newly married young couple had arrived at their hotel late in the afternoon, and had been shown up to their luxurious honeymoon suite. At long last they were alone. The bridegroom put his arms round his wife and said expectantly: 'Shall we go to bed now? Or would you rather stay up late and watch the 5.40 pm news on BBC 1?'

Hospitals

A man woke up after an operation and through a mist saw a

figure standing by his bed. 'Was my operation a success, doctor?' he whispered. 'I don't know old chap,' said the figure. 'I'm St Peter.'

A young couple got married and nine months later the wife went into hospital to have their baby. The young husband was pacing anxiously up and down in the hospital waiting-room when a nurse rushed in. 'Mr Jones,' she cried, 'many congratulations. You have got a son.' 'Amazing,' said Mr Jones looking at his watch, 'nine months exactly to the minute.'

Half an hour later the same nurse rushed in again. 'Mr Jones, Mr Jones, wonderful news. You have also got a daughter.' 'Amazing,' said Mr Jones again looking at his watch which now showed 9.45 pm. 'Nine months exactly to the minute.'

Another half an hour went by when the excited nurse ran into the room shouting: 'It's triplets and this time, it's another boy.' 'Amazing,' said Mr Jones looking at his watch, 'nine months to the exact minute.' So saying he picked up his hat and coat and made for the door. 'Where are you going?' asked the nurse. 'I'm off to have a quick drink,' he replied. 'There's nothing more due now until 11.15 pm!'

Hotel

The driver of one of those huge juggernauts was driving through the night and thought he would stop off somewhere for a few hours sleep. He tried one or two lodgings he knew in a town through which he was passing but there were no vacancies. He then tried the various pubs and small hotels but they too were full up. Finally, in desperation he decided to try a large luxurious five-star hotel, although he knew he could not afford their usual high prices. So he plucked up courage and walked up to the receptionist – a smart young man in black coat and striped trousers. 'Excuse me,' said the lorry driver, 'but do you have any special terms for long-distance drivers?' 'Yes,' replied the young man without any hesitation. 'F . . . Off!'

Irish stories

My stepfather was an Irishman from Tipperary and was I suppose fairly typical – genial and friendly but with an explosive temper, easily aroused. I'm not sure what he would have thought of the modern spate of Irish stories. I suspect he would have enjoyed telling them himself but resented being told them – at any rate by an Englishman. I must say they do make me laugh though I take care not to tell them to any of my Irish friends. I suppose with all the horrors being perpetrated in Northern Ireland they are rather 'sick'. But ridicule can act as useful anti-propaganda. Remember how as soon as war was declared Tommy Handley unleashed a series of anti-Hitler jokes which would never have been allowed by the BBC against a foreign statesman in time of peace. One good thing about the Irish stories is that they are short. I cannot resist telling one or two, all of which start with: 'Did you hear about the Irishman who . . .'

1. Was told to take his car in for a service, but got it stuck in the church door.
2. Drove his car into a river and when asked why, said a policeman had stopped him and told him to dip his headlights.
3. Thought that a Royal Enfield was a place where the Queen kept her chickens.
4. Was ordered to blow up a car and burnt his lips on the exhaust pipe.
5. Was found drinking a glass of beer on the roof of a pub. When asked why, he said he had been told that drinks were on the house.
6. Was accused of raping a girl and was lined up in an identity parade. The girl was then brought into the yard where the row of men were standing and the Irishman pointed to her and said: 'That's her!'
7. Had his right ear cut off in an accident on a building site. He and his mate Paddy were looking for it in all the rubble when Paddy picked up an ear. 'Here it is,' he called out. 'No,' said the Irishman who had lost the ear, 'that's not it. Mine had a cigarette behind it!'

8. Was playing in a game of soccer which was being televised. He scored a penalty for his side, but missed it on the
action replay.

9. Came home unexpectedly from work and found his wife
in the arms of his best friend. He rushed to a drawer, took
out a revolver, and pointed it at his own head. 'This is too
much,' he cried, 'I am going to shoot myself.' At this his
wife began to laugh. 'I don't know what you are laughing
at,' he said to her. 'You're next.'

And finally, there was the world champion tobogganist
hurtling down the Cresta Run at over 60 mph. At one of the
worst corners he had a terrible accident. He met an Irishman
Coming up!

Marriage

A husband and wife were arguing as so many do about
money – or the lack of it. 'We've simply got to economise,'
said the husband. 'If only you could learn about food we
could sack the cook.' 'In that case,' said the wife, 'learn
about making love and we can sack the chauffeur.'

On most Sundays when I am at home I take our Yorkshire
terrier Mini for a walk in Regent's Park. We usually go
alongside the zoo and see the elephants swaying from side to
side and sniff the pungent smell of the foxes. It always makes
me think of the man and wife who went one day to the zoo.
The wife got too close to the bars of the gorilla's cage, and the
gorilla dragged her screaming through the bars. He began to
rip off her clothing with the obvious intention of raping her.
'Help, help,' she cried to her husband, as she stood starkers
in the gorilla's arms. 'What shall I do?' 'Tell him you've got a
headache as you always do to me!' replied the husband
unsympathetically!

Misprints

Under a picture of the late Sir Francis Chichester was the
following caption: 'The great yachtsman Sir Francis
Chichester who with his 24-foot cutter *circumcised* the world.'

The treasurer of a cricket club sent out a notice to members at the beginning of a new season. It regretted that due to inflation the annual subscription would have to go up by two pounds per anum. (His secretary evidently could not spell.) A few days later came a letter from one of the members who said that he would prefer to go on paying through the *nose*.

Political

Mrs Thatcher was addressing the annual Conservative Ladies' Conference at the Royal Albert Hall. She emphasised that difficult times lay ahead and that the Tories would have a real fight on their hands. 'Ladies,' she cried, 'we have taken it lying down long enough. From now on we must stand with our backs to the wall.'

While Harold Wilson was Prime Minister the Queen discussed with him the question of giving him a State funeral were he to die suddenly. 'No, thank you, Mam,' he replied, 'the vast expense and trouble would not be justified. You see, Mam, I shall only be there for three days.'

Mrs Gandhi went on a State visit to Singapore and with the Prime Minister Lee Kwan Yew was watching a military parade. They were sitting together under a canopy, when suddenly the skies darkened, there was a clap of thunder and down came a tropical storm. The parade ground was soon flooded and the rain was so heavy that it came through the canopy under which Mrs Gandhi was sitting and she got drenched. Remarkably the Prime Minister was lucky and no rain fell on him, although he was only a few feet from her. So he apologised profusely to Mrs Gandhi for the fact that he was dry and she was sopping wet. 'Thank you,' she replied, as servants rushed forward to help dry her, 'but I still don't understand why it didn't Lee Kwan Yew!'

Quickies

What was the nickname given to a well-known judge who had no thumb – Justice fingers.

A man rang up the rodent officer at the local town hall to complain that his house was overrun by homosexual mice. 'What shall I do to dispose of them?' he asked. 'Get a pouffy cat,' was the reply.

A man always told people that his Cockney wife was really a Scandinavian. When they expressed surprise he explained that 'She eats like a Norse.'

What would you call a Frenchman at a circus whose act was to be shot out of a canon?
Napoleon Blownapart.

What's got six eyes and can't see?
Three blind mice.

What do you call a deaf elephant?
Anything you like. He won't hear you.

Religion

A Protestant vicar, a Catholic priest and a Rabbi were all having an argument as to which of them was the better person and nearest to God. 'Nearest to God, you say,' said the Rabbi, 'I *am* God.' At this the other two roared with laughter. 'All right,' said the Rabbi, 'come with me and I'll prove it.' So curiously they went with him down to the red light district of the town. The Rabbi knocked on a door and a luscious blonde opened it. '*God*,' she said, 'Are you here again?'

School

A public school is a place where you make friends for life and this is one of the reasons why I am so grateful to Eton. Almost anywhere I go I seem to run into an old friend or acquaintance, and most of my very close friends have lasted forty-five years or so since we were at Eton together. Of course you can also make enemies, though these don't often last for life. Unlike the two very distinguished Old Boys who had hated each other at school, and had made a point of avoiding each other ever since. Over the years they rose to the top in their respective professions – one becoming an Admiral, the other a Bishop.

As bad luck would have it they both had to attend an official ceremony at Windsor which required full ceremonial dress. There was a special train from Paddington and they were both pacing up and down the platform. The Bishop, an extremely portly figure was in his apron and gaiters, and the Admiral in full dress uniform. The Bishop spotted the Admiral and was surprised to recognise his old enemy. Determined to continue the feud and score off the Admiral, he approached him and said: 'Excuse me, Station Master, but could you tell me what time this train leaves for Windsor?' The Admiral was taken aback for a moment but suddenly realised who the Bishop was. 'Yes, madam,' he replied 'it goes at 11.15 but in your present state I would advise you not to travel!'

Race

I know that some people dislike racial stories and consider that they do harm to race relations. But there always have been stories about Jews, Scotsmen, Irishmen and so on. So, provided they are not malicious and are funny I can see no real harm in them. For instance I was told this story up in Bradford where they have a very large Pakistani community. A young Yorkshire boy arrived late at school one morning. 'I am sorry I am late teacher,' he said, 'But I had to get my own breakfast.' 'All right, Johnny,' said his teacher. 'Sit down. We are doing geography this morning, and have been talking about the division of India and Pakistan. Can you tell me where the Pakistan border is?' 'Yes, Miss,' said Johnny. 'He's in bed with Mum. That's why I had to get my own breakfast!'

Shaggy dog stories

A circus was doing very badly. Audiences were dwindling and the proprietor was losing so much money that he realised that unless drastic action were taken he would have to close down. So he summoned all his staff and asked them to think up some publicity gimmick which would bring the crowds in. After a lot of discussion the elephant trainer came up with this idea. 'My old elephant Jumbo is very obstinate and won't obey anyone except me. Why don't we offer a prize of fifty pounds to anyone who can make him sit down in the ring. I guarantee he will just stand there and refuse to budge unless *I* tell him to do it.' The proprietor thought this was a great stunt so plastered the town with leaflets and handbills announcing that on Saturday night there would be this sensational competition to see who could make Jumbo sit down. Prize fifty pounds.

On Saturday night the circus was packed out. There was standing room only. The proprietor was delighted as he counted his takings. After the interval the ringmaster announced the competition and Jumbo was brought into the ring by his trainer. He stood in the middle of the ring and the audience were invited to step in one by one and see if they could make him sit down in thirty minutes. There was a rush to try and people tried everything. They pulled his trunk, twisted his tail and shouted various words of command. But to no avail. Jumbo just stood there. So after twenty-nine minutes the ringmaster announced that with one minute to go there was just time for one more person to try. A small man stepped into the ring carrying a ladder. This he placed against the elephant's hind quarters and climbed up. When he got to the top, he lifted up the elephants's tail, and gave him a tremendous kick up the arse. The elephant with a scream of pain immediately sat down. So the small man climbed down his ladder, collected fifty pounds from the ringmaster and left the ring to uproarious applause from the audience.

Although he had had to fork out fifty pounds the proprietor had made a killing on the night. He was so pleased in fact that he asked the elephant trainer to think out another scheme for the following Saturday. The trainer said he had an absolute certainty which no one could possibly win. The task would be to make Jumbo nod his head up and down, and then shake it sideways. 'He'll never do that for anyone,' said the trainer. 'He wouldn't even do it for me. Your fifty pounds will be quite safe.'

So the same procedure was adopted the next Saturday night and once again the circus tent was packed. At the interval the audience were again told what they had to do, and were invited to try their hand for half an hour. Hundreds of them came into the ring and tried everything to make Jumbo nod his head, then shake it. But he just stood there, ignoring all their efforts.

Finally, with one minute to go the ringmaster announced there was only time for one more person to try. Once again the same small man stepped into the ring with his ladder. This time he placed it against Jumbo's shoulder and climbed up. He took hold of Jumbo's ear and whispered into it: 'Do you remember what I did to you last Saturday?' Jumbo nodded his head up and down. The audience were amazed. The small man then whispered into Jumbo's ear: 'Do you want me to do it again?' At this Jumbo shook his head vigorously from side to side. The audience cheered, the small man climbed down the ladder, pocketed another fifty pounds and left the ring. A just reward for his remembering that simple adage: 'An elephant never forgets'.

Before the start of a needle village match, the home captain found he was one short. In desperation he was looking round the ground for someone he could rope in to play when he spotted an old horse grazing quietly in the field next door. So he went up to him and asked him if he would like to make up the side. The horse stopped eating and said: 'Well, I haven't played for some time and am a bit out of practice but if you're pushed, I'll certainly help you out', and so saying jumped over the fence and sat down in a deckchair in front of the pavilion.

The visitors lost the toss and the home side batted first, the horse being put in last. They were soon 23 for 9 and the horse made his way to the wicket wearing those sort of leather shoes horses have on when they are pulling a roller or a mower. He soon showed his eye was well in and hit the bowling all over the field. When he wasn't hitting sixes he was galloping for quick singles and never once said 'neigh' when his partner called him for a run. Finally he was out hoof before wicket for a brilliant 68, and the home side had made 99.

When the visitors batted the home captain put the horse in the deep and he saved many runs by galloping round the boundary and hoofing the ball back to the wicket-keeper. However the visitors were not losing any wickets and were soon 50 for 0. The home captain had tried all his regular bowlers in vain when he suddenly thought of the horse. He had batted brilliantly and now was fielding better than anyone. At least he could do no worse than the other bowlers. So he called out to him: 'Horse, would you like to take the next over at the vicarage end?' The horse looked surprised. 'Of course I wouldn't,' he replied. 'Whoever heard of a horse who could BOWL?'

Transport

A man was motoring along a main road when he saw a very attractive blonde by the side of the road thumbing a lift. So he stopped and asked her to get into his car. As they were going along, in order to make conversation, he asked her what she did. 'Oh, I'm a witch,' she replied casually. The motorist was surprised to say the least. 'I just don't believe it,' he said. 'Can you prove it?' Saying nothing the blonde put her hand on his knee, then slowly started to run her fingers up the inside of his thigh. AND HE IMMEDIATELY TURNED INTO A LAY-BY!

The wife of a keen motorist was a terrible 'back seat driver'. She used to keep up a running commentary on what she thought her husband should and should not do. 'Mind that lorry; there's a girl coming out of that turning; look out for that child,' etc etc. It used to go on non-stop, and drove the poor man crazy. One day they were out in the car and the usual advice was coming from the back. After a while the driver noticed that there was silence and gratefully drove on in peace. Suddenly a policeman on a motorbike drew alongside and signalled him to pull into the side of the road. When he had stopped he unwound his window, and the policeman got off his bike and said breathlessly. 'Excuse me, sir, your back door swung open a few miles back and a lady fell out on to the road. I'm glad to say she's not hurt.' 'Oh,' said the driver, 'that must be my wife. She must have leant against the door and fallen out. Thank goodness for that. I thought for a moment I had gone deaf.'

It was a very foggy night in London and all the traffic was crawling along at about five miles an hour. For safety's sake a man thought he would walk right behind a bus which he knew was going his way, and so be protected from oncoming traffic. When he got home he told his wife what he had done and added . . . 'at least I saved my usual 15p bus fare.' 'Why didn't you walk behind a taxi,' said the wife, 'and save £2.50?'

A man was belting along a main road at about eighty miles per hour, when just ahead of him he saw a tractor with two men on it coming slowly out of a gate and on to the road. Realising that if he went straight on he would hit the tractor, he swung violently to his left and shot through the gate into the field from which the tractor had come. He bumped along the field parallel to the road for several yards then noticed a gap in the hedge. So he drove through it back on to the road and continued his journey at speed, as if nothing had happened. 'You know George,' said one of the men on the tractor to the other, 'we only just got out of that field in time!'

A Mini had broken down and its owner was standing disconsolately by the side of the road. A very posh new Jaguar drew up and its driver asked if he could help. The Mini-owner said he did not know what was wrong, so the man in the Jaguar said: 'OK, I'll give you a tow – I've got a thin nylon rope in my boot. I'll go along slowly but if anything is wrong blow your horn like mad.' So they set off slowly and were cruising along at about 30 mph when a big red Mercedes passed them at great speed.

This nettled the Jaguar driver who thought that for the sake of Queen and Country he should show that British was best. So forgetting he had the Mini in tow he set off in pursuit and soon reached 100 mph and was gaining on the Mercedes. The poor man in the Mini wondered what on earth was happening. From the sedate speed of 30 mph he was suddenly hurtling along at an incredible pace, and his small car was swaying and jumping all over the place. Remembering what he had been told he started to hoot like mad.

As he did so, they shot past a police car parked in a lay-by. The police driver was amazed and quickly got on to the radio to speak to another police car three miles up the road. 'Look out,' he said, 'there's a crazy road race going on and they're coming towards you very fast. There's a big red Mercedes doing well over 100 mph. Close behind and just about to pass him is a man in a Jaguar. And believe it or not in a Mini nearly touching the Jaguar's rear bumper is a frightened looking man sounding his horn like mad, trying to pass them both!'

Ted Moult is a lovely character and was a most amusing companion on the various tours or series we did together with the *Treble Chance Quiz*. We always used to do a warm-up session for the audience before the recording of the show began. In his slow lazy drawl he used to tell some splendid stories and this one was my particular favourite.

A man was driving his car through a country village when it suddenly spluttered and came to a halt. He looked at his fuel gauge and realised that he had run out of petrol. He spotted a man sitting on a bench outside a pub so went up to him and asked him if he would be very kind and give the car a push to the village garage about two hundred yards up the street. The man very decently agreed to help and with much puffing and blowing managed to push the car to the garage.

The driver, who had remained in his seat in order to steer the car, gave the petrol attendant a five pound note and asked him to fill the car up with five pounds' worth of petrol. When he had done so, the driver turned to the man who had helped him and who was standing close by looking quite exhausted.

'I'm sorry,' said the driver, 'but I have spent all the money

I had with me on the petrol, so I have none to give you. But do you smoke by any chance?' 'Yes, I do,' gasped the man between breaths. 'Well,' said the driver, 'I should give it up if I were you. You look half-knackered!' And so saying he wound up his window and drove off!

A little girl kept biting her nails and her mother told her that if she didn't stop doing it she would grow very fat. The next day she and her mother were on a bus, and sitting opposite them was a very pregnant blonde. The little girl kept staring at her. After a while the blonde got fed up and said to the girl: 'What are you staring at me for? Do you know me?' 'No,' said the little girl, 'but I know what you've been doing!'

A motorist was lost near Guildford and stopped to ask a passer-by the way. Motorist: 'Do you know the Hog's Back?' Passer-by: 'No. I didn't know he'd been away!'

Last Over or Who's been a lucky boy, then?

As the time came for me to bowl this last 'over' I began reflecting on my past – always a dangerous occupation. But I am glad that I did so, because once again it was brought home to me how very lucky I have been all through my life. The last two months especially have constantly reminded me of the variety of my life, and the different cross-sections of people whom I have met and been able to call my friends.

I must admit that when checking through my diary for November and December it looks rather like a gastronomic orgy. Take cricket. There were two excellent lunches organised by firms who give great help to cricket, the Wrigley Company and John Haig. The former give generous financial support to young cricketers, the latter sponsor those excellent competitions for clubs and villages.

It is at gatherings such as these that one realises how cricket seems to bring out the best in people. Why *are* cricketers – and even cricket writers and broadcasters – so nice? There can surely be no other game in the world that so enriches the lives of those who are connected with it or play it.

There was another evening reception for the official opening of the Lord's Cricket School by Gubby Allen. As the gossip writers would say 'anyone who is anyone in cricket' was there to see Derek Shackleton bowl the first ball to Colin Cowdrey. It is quite easily the best cricket school I have ever seen. It has superb lighting and six nets with varying degrees of pace and spin. And vital in our search for fast bowlers, there is a long run-up for the bowlers of at least seventeen yards, which many people would consider to be the maximum necessary for *any* fast bowler even in a Test Match.

The school was paid for by members of MCC with some help from commerce and a magnificent contribution from that lover and patron of cricket Jack Hayward. In recognition of this the playing area is known as the Hayward Hall. Jack told me he was off that week back to his home in the Bahamas to rehearse for the annual pantomime out there. He was going to play one of the Ugly Sisters in *Cinderella* and I was able to give him two gags to use in the 'dressing for the ball' scene. One ugly sister to the other:

'How do you like my religious dress?'

'Religious dress?'

'Yes – lo(w) and behold.'

'Well, I call *mine* a barbed wire dress – it protects the property without obscuring the view.'

I wonder if he used them!

I have always acknowledged how lucky I was to go to Eton, which to me has proved to be the best trade union in the world. Wherever I go on my job I always seem to run into an Old Etonian and on numerous occasions this has broken the ice or gained an *entrée* – especially if he is a highly respected official and I greet him as 'Fruity' or 'Jumbo' or whatever I used to call him at Eton.

Anyhow, in November I was invited to speak at the annual dinner of the Eton Rackets Club which brought me into contact with a lot of my Etonian friends. Luckily many of them were quite young so quite a few of my hoary jokes were new to them. Like the old one of the housemaster's wife who attended a concert at which the headmaster's wife recited a piece of French poetry. When she had finished the housemaster's wife applauded loudly and turned to her companion. 'Didn't she recite that well? And how wise not to attempt the French accent!'

The biggest occasion during the autumn was a theatrical one – the lunch for one thousand guests given by Peter Saunders at the Savoy to celebrate the twenty-fifth year of *The Mousetrap*. It was a marvellous opportunity to meet again so many of the stage personalities with whom I have worked from time to time in the last thirty-two years. Pauline and I gave a lift home to Evelyn Laye and Anna Neagle – how's that for three beautiful ladies in one taxi?

Then there were Jack and Cis Courtneidge holding court
in a corner, Cis as vivacious as ever, and Jack with that lazy
drawl of his asking me about the Packer business. Another
mad cricket enthusiast was Celia Johnson and Dinah Sheri-
dan too, though she admitted that she was not *quite* as keen as
Celia. She said that Celia stops to watch every village cricket
match which she comes across in the summer. Vera Lynn,
and Tommy Trinder – for once without his hat, and in spite
of Fulham in his usual good form – represented variety. It
seems impossible to keep cricket out of this because Andrew
Cruickshank unexpectedly is a fan and so of course is
Michael Denison who is a regular at Lord's. Dulcie Gray
was with him, though I don't know how she finds time to be
social with her acting, her radio part in *Waggoners' Walk* and
writing her thrillers. There were two regular Arsenal supporters there – impresario Peter Bridge and Ian Wallace. I
always enjoy meeting them so that I can reel off the Arsenal
side which I used to watch in the thirties:

> *Bastin, James, Drake, Jack, Hulme,*
> *Copping, Roberts, Crayston,*
> *Hapgood, Male,*
> *Moss*

That was the line-up as far as I can remember, and unlike
today they remained in that formation right through the
match. It must have made George Allison's job as commentator so much easier than that of the modern commentators.

Two of the best of our light comedy actors are as amusing
off the stage as on, Donald Sinden with his delicious fruity
voice and Leslie Phillips with that wicked leer in his eyes.
And then someone we had not seen for a long time but
looking just as young and beautiful – Sally Anne Howes,
whose father Bobby was a great friend of Pauline's father.
And of course tinkling his white piano as an accompaniment
to the champagne and smoked salmon was Ian Stewart,
whom I remember playing the second piano opposite Car-
roll Gibbons *before* the war!

And finally, the host himself Peter Saunders, another

cricket enthusiast and a kind, generous person completely unspoilt by his great success. He is the only one of my friends who has a telephone in his car. But unlike Lew Grade he only has *one*. So if you ring him up you can't be asked to hold on 'as he is on the *other* line'. I am afraid all this has read rather like a mixture of *Jennifer's Diary* and Nigel Dempster. But it is an illustration of how lucky I have been to know so many fascinating people in the world of showbusiness.

This lunch also emphasised the strong link which exists between the stage and cricket. Perhaps it is not so surprising as they are both forms of the arts requiring great skill and technique, utter dedication and hard work. At the same time they both offer the individual the chance of showing off his talents, while remaining the member of a team. The affiliation goes back a long way. I suppose the most famous actor cricketer of all was Sir C. Aubrey Smith, that grand old film actor, who actually captained England in the first ever Test against South Africa in 1889. He was a fine fast medium bowler, whose slanting run-up earned him the nickname of Round-the-corner Smith. He founded the Hollywood Cricket Club and ran a flourishing cricket team which included such actors as Nigel Bruce, Ronald Coleman and Boris Karloff.

Sir George Robey was a member of MCC and in the twenties Old Harrovian Sir Gerald Du Maurier was a regular attendant at the Eton and Harrow match at Lord's. Other frequent watchers at Lord's over the past forty years or so have been Clifford Mollison, Arthur Askey, Richard Attenborough, Michael Denison, Ian Carmichael, David Tomlinson and of course Trevor Howard – a good all-round club cricketer who always insists that any film contract which he signs gives him time off to see the Lord's Test. He has watched MCC and England teams all over the world, as has that remarkable nonagenarian writer of farces Ben Travers. Another writer who adored cricket was the late Terence Rattigan, who was himself good enough to play for Harrow.

The Stage Cricket Society has always produced an enthusiastic side and I remember playing against them shortly after the war for the Cross Arrows at Lord's. They were captained by that ace 'villain' Garry Marsh who was a determined left-handed bat and they could also call on the slow left arm wiles of Lauri Lupino Lane, and the batting skills of Cyril Luckham.

But of course nowadays it is the Lord's Taverners who give the actors a chance to perform before large crowds on Sundays throughout the summer. I wouldn't dare to attempt to grade them in any particular order, but there are some pretty useful actor-cricketers playing today. As batsmen there are John Alderton, Tim Rice, Willie Rushton and David Frost. The bowlers include Brian Rix, Roy Castle, Tom Baker, Michael Jayston, William-Sccchhh-Franklyn and Harry Secombe. The latter is in fact an all-rounder in more senses than one, and in spite of being so shortsighted can give the ball an almighty tonk. To guard the timbers today there are Ian Lavender and Ed Stewart, but some years back now there were the two bravest wicket-keepers whom I have ever seen, Eric Sykes and the late John Slater. Both of them took far more balls on the chest than they ever did in their gloves!

Then there are the mad keen cricketers who are always ready to turn up and play in these charity games. Their skills may vary but their enthusiasm and light-hearted approach make the Lord's Taverners' matches the fun and success that they always are. People like Bernard Cribbens, Gerald Harper, Michael Aspel, Pete Murray, Tim Brook-Taylor, Ronnie Corbett, Leslie Crowther and Nicholas Parsons. What a cast.

There is just one other player I must mention – Norman Wisdom – whose son incidentally has played for Sussex. Some years ago Norman was playing for the Taverners against an Old England XI at Lord's. He was batting, and making the crowd roar with laughter at his antics, doing his falls and funny walks. An old MCC member who had been dozing peacefully in the sun, was suddenly awoken by an extra loud burst of laughter. He looked up to see Norman falling about all over the place, and turned to his neighbour and said: 'I don't know how good a cricketer that chap is, but he ought to be a comedian!'

My post has also brought back some memories including

an invitation to dinner with the Junior Common Room at New College, Oxford, where I had spent three such happy years in the thirties. So far as I know I still hold two records there. First, I am the only rugger player to have scored a try for the college in a macintosh, which a spectator had lent me to cover my confusion when my shorts had been ripped off. And secondly, I must still be the only person to have had his trousers removed and thrown through the window of the senior common room, where they landed on a table round which the dons were sitting drinking port.

And of course there is the wonderful variety of Christmas cards. Like those from some of my old Grenadier staff when I was Technical Adjutant in the 2nd Battalion Grenadiers from 1941 to 1945. The nice thing is that they still sign themselves with the nicknames which I bestowed on them. My scout car driver Hengist, my chief clerk Honest Joe, the driver of the store truck Tremble – so called because it was the name of a decrepit old butler whom he played in a sketch in one of our battalion revues. And my soldier servant (as the Brigade of Guards called a batman) Pasha whose surname was Ruston. One ex-guardsman sent me an old programme of the revue we did at Seigburg in Germany in the autumn of 1945. It was called *What About It Then?*, and to show you the standard of its humour, here is one of the jokes which I remember.

'What's the difference between funny and fanny?'

'Well you can feel funny without feeling fanny, but you can't feel fanny without feeling funny.'

And a card from an old friend Frank Copping took me back to my few years as a city gent, disguised in a bowler hat, with a rolled umbrella, and in a pinstripe suit too tight under the armpits. Frank ran the cable department where I started when I joined our family coffee business. He nursed me and tried to teach me business methods without, I fear, a great deal of success. But I did enjoy ringing him up from the next office and pretending to be an irate Italian agent of ours called Enrico Colombino; not that my Italian accent was all that hot.

And always most welcome are the cards from all the friends I have made in the cricketing countries round the

world, including this year one from Mike Brearley and Ken
Barrington in Pakistan. I got to know Brearlers well when he
toured South Africa with Mike Smith's MCC team in 1964,
straight from his triumphs on the Fenners pitch at Cam-
bridge. For some strange reason he hardly made a run on the
tour and indeed looked a complete novice. But I shall always
remember how well he took it, and never showed the terrific
disappointment which he must have felt – fortified perhaps
by his triumphs at the bridge table with Charles Fortune,
David Brown and myself.

Barrers was on at least six of the MCC tours which I went
on, and he was always a tremendous influence for good both
on and off the field. A one hundred per cent fighter on it, and
a great mimic and joker off it. His take-off of W. G. Grace in
the nets is a classic – complete with MCC cap with a button
on top, beard and towels stuffed inside his shirt to give him
the necessary girth! I would say that he and Brearley should
make an ideal partnership.

And this is perhaps the best place for me to give you my
selection of the best all-round captain of England during my
years of commentating since the war. As you have probably
discovered, it has been a very difficult task. They
all – inevitably, since they are human – have their good and
bad points. The circumstances in which they played and the
quality of the teams which they led, also varied considerably.
For instance I have a feeling that with the material of the
Hutton/May teams in the mid-fifties under his command,
Freddie Brown might well have proved the best captain of
them all. In fact, it's rather fun to create the perfect captain
made up of the best characteristics of some of the others.
How about a captain with:

the fighting qualities and leadership of Freddie Brown
the unflappable character of Mike Smith
the tactical ability of Ray Illingworth
the playing skill of Len Hutton
the magic PR touch with the media and the crowds of
Tony Greig
the off-the-field charisma of Colin Cowdrey.

I reckon he would have been *some* captain, though I

suspect its perfectly possible to mingle some of the other characteristics and produce an equally fine specimen.

But sticking to one man, I have given pride of place to Ray Illingworth. He may not have been the establishment's favourite man, but he does possess most of the essential qualities. A determined character with a dry sense of humour, leadership, tactical skill, playing ability and excellent public relations with the media. He loses a few marks for his off-the-field image, but as I have said he went out to Australia with one thing only in mind – to win back the Ashes – and he did so. Two other tough and single-minded captains did likewise – Douglas Jardine and Len Hutton. The nice guys of this world like the Gilligans, Allens, Mays and Smiths perhaps lack the killer instinct that a captain must have to win. Anyway I am sure that some of you have made out equally good cases for people like May, Cowdrey or possibly Brearley on his initial but successful record so far.

The BBC always have lots of parties at Christmas time and this year in December the director-general, Ian Trethowan, gave a delightful dinner party at the Television Centre in honour of Antony Craxton, who was retiring from the Corporation.

'Crackers' was brought up near Lord's in a musical family, but his first love was always cricket. We used to play a lot in charity matches and for all I know he may have been a very good leg-spinner. Unfortunately the ball never pitched, so I shall never find out! For years he was our TV cricket producer and we had much fun and enjoyment. Like me he thinks there is more to cricket than what goes on out in the middle, and he was always on the lookout for the unusual shot of off-the-field activities. He produced some of the best leg-pulls on Jim Swanton, like the time when the election of a Pope coincided with a Test Match at Lord's, where Jim and I were the commentators.

In St Peter's Square, Rome, the crowds were massed waiting for the tell-tale puff of white smoke from one of the Vatican chimneys which would be the sign that the Cardinals had made their decision. At the same time at Lord's a chimney in the old Lord's Tavern caught fire and black smoke belched out. Quick as a flash Crackers had a camera pointing at the black smoke. 'There you are,' I was able to say, 'Jim Swanton has been elected Pope.' Or the occasion when one of his cameras spotted John Warr and his fiancée Valerie sitting together in the grandstand – Warr and Piece!

When he left cricket, Crackers became the Royal Producer, culminating in his triumphant broadcast of the Jubilee Service in St Paul's, which by coincidence was his two hundredth Royal TV occasion. Many of his friends were at the dinner, John Snagge, Michael Standing, Peter West, Cliff Morgan, Richard Baker, Robert Hudson and myself all representing the commentators. As you can imagine there was much reminiscing and Crackers actually told an announcer's gaffe which I had not heard before – I thought I knew them all!

Here it is: An announcer was introducing a concert. 'Tonight's concert,' he said, 'will be given by the Ceffield Shity Police Band' . . . After he had finished the rest of the announcement his producer told him what he had said, and that listeners were already ringing up to complain. The producer advised him not to apologise as it would only draw attention to his mistake. But he ordered the poor announcer to be sure to get the name of the band right in the closing announcement. So when the end of the programme arrived the announcer – now a bag of nerves – steeled himself and came out with: 'You have just been listening to a concert given by the Sheffield City Police Band. The concert was broadcast from the Ceffield Shity Hall.'

But, in spite of all my friends, the true foundation of my happiness has been my wife, my family and my home. By the time you read this Pauline and I will, I hope, have celebrated our Pearl wedding. I would just like to thank her for her continued love and understanding. Also for her patience with my jokes, my many absences from home, and my possible over-indulgence in work. My family, thank goodness, have given me few problems, only boundless joy and amusement. Barry and Clare live in their own homes in London, and Andrew is still working in Sydney, so that Ian and Joanna are the only ones still at home. But almost every weekend we have a family reunion for Sunday lunch when we laugh, quarrel, play cards and table tennis, and tuck in to roast beef and Yorkshire pudding (when the housekeeping account is not too heavily overdrawn). So thanks too to them for making me so happy and I forgive them for trying to get their own back on me – they now tell *me* far worse jokes than I ever told *them*.

It is interesting that my way of life and connections with the entertainment world have obviously influenced their choice of jobs and careers. Not one of them is a member of any of the professions. Nor do any of them do nine to five humdrum office jobs. Barry's pop group 'Design' broke up amicably in 1976. He now has a small music publishing business, records the odd single or jingle and does a first-class cabaret act which includes all the well-known Noël Coward songs which he delivers crisply and clearly just like the Master. He also still composes songs full of melody and is just waiting for one of them to 'take off'. It is as a composer that I see his future. Don't forget the name, Barry Alexander, so called, as I have mentioned earlier, because there is already a Barry Johnston in Equity.

Clare after three years in Australia now works as a PR executive in London, and one of her accounts is a famous TV and recording company. She is much travelled and she and I have a 'visited the most countries' contest. Since her return from Australia via South, Central and North America she has edged ahead and her total is now fifty-three against my forty-four.

Andrew worked in Foyles Book Shop over here and then three years ago left for Sydney where he now works for a worldwide English publishing firm. And to keep up the entertainment theme Ian – after a year's varied experience in Australia as a messenger for ABC, a jackaroo on an estate, a 'showie' on bumper cars and a researcher for a mining firm – now has a job with a large group of record shops. The nice thing about all their jobs is that they got them on their own merits without any help or influence from Dad. Incidentally, whenever she has time off from running the house, looking after Joanna or her charities like the Life-Boats and the Mentally Handicapped Children, Pauline does a spot of photography at which she is highly trained and expert.

And finally our home in St John's Wood where we are so marvellously looked after by our wonderful housekeeper Cally. What we would do without her I don't know. She and Pauline between them continue to look after Joanna with loving care and devotion. As a result Joanna – now aged twelve – is a happy pupil at the Gatehouse Learning Centre in Bethnal Green, which is so efficiently and kindly run by its remarkable founder Mrs Wallbank. We have been in St John's Wood now for thirty years and I could wish for no more friendly nor delightful place in which to live – remarkably peaceful and still with a village atmosphere, although only ten minutes away from Piccadilly Circus by car. The large garden is an added joy, not just for us but also for our Yorkshire terrier, Mini, who spends her life chasing (but never catching) grey squirrels. I am the destroyer in the garden – I weed, mow and light the bonfire. Pauline and our faithful friend Mr Webber do the creative work. The colourful result of their labours is enjoyed as much by our neighbours as by ourselves.

So there we are. I hope you have stayed with me until close of play, and have enjoyed, or at least tolerated, the meanderings of a remarkably happy and lucky person, to whom life – like cricket – is a funny game and still A LOT OF FUN.

St John's Wood
Christmas 1977

Index

STAR BESTSELLERS

0352 309350	**WHISPERS** Dean R Koontz (GF)	1.95*
0352 310804	**ROGUE OF GOR** John Norman (Sci. Fantasy)	**2.25***
0352 310413	**AFTERMATH** Roger Williams (GF)	1.60
0352 310170	**A MAN WITH A MAID** Anonymous (GF)	1.60*
0352 310928	**A MAN WITH A MAID VOL. II** Anonymous (GF)	1.75
0352 395621	**THE STUD** Jackie Collins (GF)	1.75
0352 300701	**LOVEHEAD** Jackie Collins (GF)	1.50
0352 398663	**THE WORLD IS FULL OF DIVORCED WOMEN** Jackie Collins (GF)	1.75
0352 398752	**THE WORLD IS FULL OF MARRIED MEN** Jackie Collins (GF)	1.75
0352 311339	**THE GARMENT** Catherine Cookson (GF)	1.25
0426 163524	**HANNAH MASSEY** Catherine Cookson (GF)	1.35
0426 163605	**SLINKY JANE** Catherine Cookson (GF)	1.25
0352 310634	**THE OFFICERS' WIVES** Thomas Fleming (GF)	2.75*
0352 302720	**DELIA OF VENUS** Anais Nin (GF)	1.50*
0352 306157	**LITTLE BIRDS** Anais Nin (GF)	1.25*
0352 310359	**BITE OF THE APPLE** Molly Parkin (GF)	1.50

*Not for sale in Canada   Prices are subject to alteration

STAR BESTSELLERS

0352 311010	**CARDINAL SINS** Andrew M. Greeley (GF)	1.95*
0352 310723	**THE ANALOG BULLET** Martin Cruz Smith (GF)	1.50*
0352 310715	**THE INDIANS WON** Martin Cruz Smith (GF)	1.50*
0352 312513	**LOVING FEELINGS** Kelly Stearn (GF)	1.75
0352 312823	**FLIGHT 902 IS DOWN** H. Fisherman & B. Schiff (Thriller)	1.95*
0352 397403	**DOG SOLDIERS** Robert Stone (Thriller)	1.95*
0352 312408	**THE WARRIOR WITHIN** S. Green (Sci. Fic.)	1.75*
0352 312491	**FRIDAY 13TH III** Michael Avallone (Horror)	1.60*
0352 312017	**SLUGS** Shaun Hutson (Horror)	1.60
0352 306866	**DEATH TRIALS** Elwyn Jones (Gen. Non. Fic.)	1.25
0352 398108	**IT'S BEEN A LOT OF FUN** Brian Johnston (Bio)	1.80
0352 311487	**BING THE HOLLOW MAN** Shepherd & Slatzer	1.75*
0352 303506	**THE UNINVITED** Clive Harold (unexplained)	1.50
0352 310022	**BARRY MANILOW** Tony Jasper (Music)	1.50
0352 301961	**A TWIST OF LENNON** Cynthia Lennon (Music)	1.25

* Not for sale in Canada   Prices are subject to alteration

STAR BESTSELLERS

0352 300965	**LONELINESS OF THE LONG-DISTANCE RUNNER** Alan Sillitoe (GF)	1.60
0352 300981	**SATURDAY NIGHT AND SUNDAY MORNING** Alan Sillitoe (GF)	1.35
0352 310863	**BEST FRIENDS** Kelly Stearn (GF)	1.75
0352 310456	**GHOSTS OF AFRICA** William Stevenson (GF)	1.95*
0352 300078	**THE FIRST DEADLY SIN** Lawrence Sanders (Thriller)	1.95*
0352 30099X	**DIRTY HARRY** Philip Rock (Thriller)	1.25*
0352 307390	**THE GOOD THE BAD AND THE UGLY** Joe Millard (Western)	1.25
0352 305231	**CROSSFIRE TRAIL** Louis L'Amour (Western)	1.25*
0352 312858	**THE SUNSET WARRIOR** Eric Van Lustbader (Sci Fic.)	1.95*
0352 312874	**SHALLOWS OF NIGHT** Eric Van Lustbader (Sci Fic.)	1.95*
0352 312866	**DAI-SAN** Eric Van Lustbader (Sci. Fic.)	1.95*
0352 309237	**101 REASONS NOT TO HAVE SEX TONIGHT** I M Potent, M.D. (Humour)	1.25*
0352 390121	**BODYGUARD OF LIES** Anthony Cave Brown (Gen Non. Fic.)	2.50*
0352 310731	**PERSONAL COMPUTERS** Peter Rodwell (Gen, Non. Fic.)	1.50

*Not for sale in Canada   Prices are subject to alteration

STAR Books are obtainable from many booksellers and newsagents. If you have any difficulty please send purchase price plus postage on the scale below to:-

Star Cash Sales
P.O. Box 11
Falmouth
Cornwall
OR
Star Book Service,
G.P.O. Box 29,
Douglas,
Isle of Man,
British Isles.

While every effort is made to keep prices low, it is sometimes necessary to increase prices at short notice. Star Books reserve the right to show new retail prices on covers which may differ from those advertised in the text or elsewhere.

Postage and Packing Rate
UK: 45p for the first book, 20p for the second book and 14p for each additional book ordered to a maximum charge of £1.63. BFPO and EIRE: 45p for the first book, 20p for the second book, 14p per copy for the next 7 books thereafter 8p per book. Overseas: 75p for the first book and 21p per copy for each additional book.